Wise Guide
Enrichment Activity
Worksheets:
Lists A-M

Student Worksheets & Teacher Answer Keys
for Wanda Sanseri's
Spell to Write and Read

Elizabeth FitzGerald, M.S.

LITHBTH Educational Services
Hayward, CA

Wise Guide Enrichment Activity Worksheets:
Lists A-M

LITHBTH Educational Services
California

Second Printing

www.swrtraining.com

ISBN 978-0-9744920-2-5

PRINTED IN THE UNITED STATES OF AMERICA

To David

*You always encourage me
to use the gifts the Lord Jesus
has given me to bless others.*

*You are my hero, my friend, and
— as you frequently remind me —
my biggest fan.*

Table of Contents

Key to Language Arts Category Codes

The activities in *The Wise Guide* fall into different categories for language learning and other curricular subjects. Many activities qualify for more than one category.

A	Art
B	Bible
G	Grammar activity
L	Listening
Ph	Phonograms
P	Punctuation
Sc	Science
V	Vocabulary
W	Writing
WB	Word-building

Foreword

Liz FitzGerald has created this helpful supplement for *The Wise Guide for Spelling* with my blessing. Going back to the days when my *Teaching Reading at Home and School* was crafted as a supplement to *Writing Road to Reading*, she became my second Endorsed Teacher Trainer. Her feedback and editing were invaluable as I transformed that work into the stand-alone program that *Spell to Write and Read* is today. Her professional training as a Speech and Language Therapist helped me understand and articulate more clearly concepts like "think-to-spell" and coarticulation. She has had a long, dedicated track record of working with the program. In addition to teaching many SWR seminars over the years, she developed the award-winning *Cursive First* program. For many years, she has been the faithful owner and moderator of the SWR Yahoo Support Group that today has over thirty-five hundred members. She has created a dynamic web site that helps explain the program and provide practical help. Her consistent dedication has helped her sense the pulse of SWR users and given her a heart to address the needs she sees.

Liz has worked to harmonize her vision for this project directly with me. She sought my permission to do the worksheets. She has provided working rough draft copies for my review and honored my suggestions. I am strongly pleased with the results. This is a powerful addition to the program. I believe this valuable resource will meet a great need for the busy educator who wants to take the fullest advantage of the various spelling enrichments in *The Wise Guide*.

Happy Teaching,

Wanda Sanseri
author of *Spell to Write and Read*

Preface

After grad school for Speech and Language Pathology, my first full-time position was as a Special Day Class Teacher for severe speech and language delayed children. With the goal of learning how to teach probably the most important subject taught in the classroom, I immediately enrolled in a graduate level training class called "How to Teach Reading." In that class I learned reading theory, group management, and that once a student could learn to decode the written text, teaching reading was really all about teaching language. As a language therapist, I found myself in familiar territory. However, I didn't learn how to unlock the mysteries of the English written code for young students until I took Wanda Sanseri's Basic Seminar for the method that would become known as Spell to Write and Read.

At the time I started teaching with Wanda's materials, we were using *The Writing Road to Reading,* and the only reinforcement activity I could assign my students was to write their spelling words in sentences; an important task, but by no means a thorough language experience. When Wanda published *The Wise Guide for Spelling* in 2000, it was filled with ideas and activities that used the spelling words as a springboard for all sorts of language learning. As we worked through the Wise Lists, my students' vocabularies and their understanding of base words and derivatives also advanced. This led to better reading comprehension as they were able to understand what they were reading and how to decode unfamiliar words. They recognized long "complicated" words as nothing but phonograms and simple syllables, all following our reliable rules.

While working with teachers in my seminars and interacting with our program users on our Yahoo Support Group, I started noticing a pattern. These teachers loved the program and the beauty of the multi-sensory approach. They worked to perfect their spelling dictation and to navigate the weekly lessons. However, they tended to overlook or skip the reinforcement activities. Their focus was merely on teaching new spelling words because they didn't have the time nor did they see the value of setting up and working through the enrichment lessons. When teachers would question why their students were not advancing as they hoped, I discovered a common denominator; they were not taking full advantage of the language lessons in *The Wise Guide.* Their students were rarely being given the opportunity to experience their spelling words in the context of the language they were expected to use for everyday reading and writing activities.

In 2012 I returned to the classroom to start teaching SWR one or two days a week. Naturally, I wanted to take full advantage of the rich bounty that *The Wise Guide* held. Since I was not working with the students every day, I developed worksheets for *The Wise Guide* activities so my students could practice their spelling words in a variety of meaningful ways, all while continuing to reinforce the multi-sensory approach. The worksheets had to be easy to understand for both the student and the parent. They incorporated grammar instruction, something teachers often feel inadequate to teach. Eventually, the material included all of the Wise Lists from A-Z. When I had my seminar students try them out, they wanted their own copies so they, too, could strengthen their language arts instruction.

My sincere gratitude goes to my Foundational Language Arts students and parents at HEART Academy, and to the Cunningham, DiNatale, Lung, and Orelup families. Without your faithful field-testing, I would only have ideas swirling around in my head and no finished materials with which to bless other SWR students and teachers. I'm so excited to include the illustrations my artistic daughter Shannon provided, and I'm thankful for her encouragement to draw a few myself. I am indebted to Wanda Sanseri for teaching me how to teach reading and spelling. She entrusted me with her program as one of her Endorsed Trainers, and she continues to invest in my life as an educator and as a daughter of the King.

May you yield rich rewards for your investment in our next generation,

Liz

Elizabeth FitzGerald, M.S.
Endorsed SWR Trainer, Northern CA

How to Use These Worksheets

I. WORKSHEET DESIGN & PURPOSE

1. **Worksheet activities match the instructions found in *The Wise Guide* ©2015.** Previous versions of *The Wise Guide* can easily be used! Just be aware there may be new activities listed in this book or changes in activity examples that aren't in an older book.

2. **If an assignment lends itself to a worksheet, it's included.**
   a. Worksheets are meant to supplement the activities in The Wise Guide, NOT to replace it. You need both!
   b. Sentence Writing Activities are included only when they are specifically reinforcing a concept just taught or where a new concept is introduced. Most sentence writing assignments can easily take place on regular paper, so a worksheet is unnecessary.

Each worksheet has both a **student version** (on the CD) and a **teacher Answer Key** (in the book).

Each worksheet clearly identifies which **Wise List** the activity came from and **the name of the activity** as you'll find it in the *Wise Guide.*

Instructions for how to complete the page as well as information about the concept being explored is included at the top of each worksheet.

Key concepts are highlighted in **bold**.

Teacher notes are often included to give more information or to help you tailor the page to the students' needs.

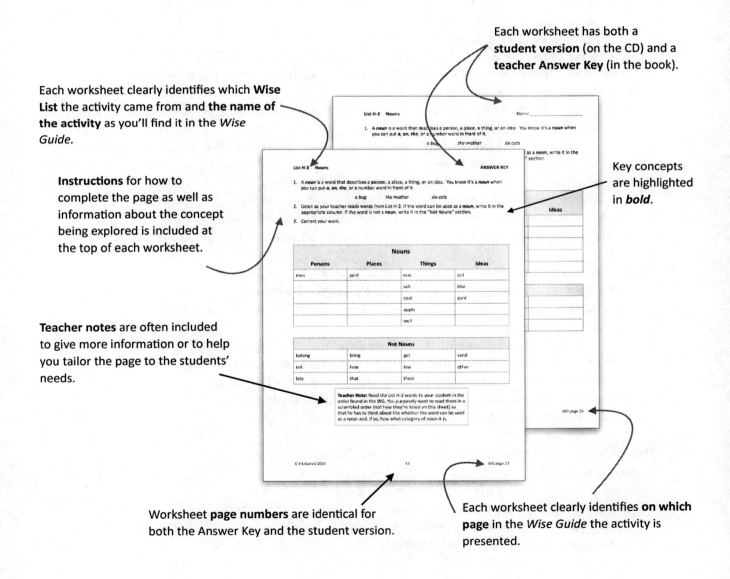

Worksheet **page numbers** are identical for both the Answer Key and the student version.

Each worksheet clearly identifies **on which page** in the *Wise Guide* the activity is presented.

3. **Reference is to a single, male student** for ease and clarity in writing. It is clearly understood that students can also be female and that a teacher might be working with a group or a class.

4. **Multiple possibilities for student answers** are often listed on the Teacher Answer Keys.
   a. These are not always an exhaustive list. You may find more options. Let us know when you do! http://www.swrtraining.com/contact-us/
   b. Usually the student is only required to come up with one answer, unless multiple options are requested in the instructions.

5. **Worksheet Instructions are written to the student**
   a. Help him read the instructions until he can do so himself.
   b. Your teaching instructions can be found in this area.

> It is critical that you have your student writing as much as possible.

6. **Writing assignments are often included as an added reinforcement.**
   a. Children master their spelling as they continue to be exposed to new words and especially in the context of sentences. They need regular practice with sentence writing.
   b. Many of the assignments ask the student to write a sentence or two using a spelling word or a derivative that they just created. This is great practice that helps solidify what they're learning and which provides you with an on-the-spot grammar lesson.
   c. Low on time? Either skip the writing or, better yet, come back later in the week and add the sentence(s) to complete the page.
   d. It is critical that you have your student writing as much as possible, so be careful that skipping these assignments doesn't become a habit. I've watched over and over as students who were omitting the sentence writing struggled...until they started including this. Both the student's reading and writing started to flourish as a result.
   e. These writing assignments may be in addition to those specifically outlined in *The Wise Guide* for writing original sentences or for taking dictation on sentences or paragraphs.

7. **Worksheets provide "Extra" pages for Primary Learning Log users.**
   a. The Primary Learning Log does not have Reference Pages for the ED rule, Contractions, Abbreviations, Prepositions, etc. The worksheets now provide you a guided lesson for completing these activities.
   b. If your student is using the Black Learning Log, use the Reference Pages in your student's Learning Log to complete the assignment and skip the worksheets; they are intended more for students who are using the Primary Log. However, when you use up your Reference Pages in the Log, you have a backup place and/or activity to continue working on the concept.

> Copying is a passive activity that does not lead to long-term mastery.

8. **The assignments require the student to write from his brain as much as possible, not to copy.**
   a. Your goal is for the student to instantly know how to spell and, therefore, write words correctly when his brain is focusing on the *content* of writing, not the *mechanics* of writing (spelling, punctuation, grammar, etc.). Copying is a passive activity that does

not lead to long-term mastery. Dynamic brain-focused activities are vital to accomplish this.

    b. These worksheets occasionally include assignments for which the student is to copy from his Learning Log. In this case, his log is a resource for finding more words that fit a concept he's working on.

II. LESSON PLANNING

1. **FIRST, start with the Wise Guide** and read through the suggested activities for the list(s) you're teaching.
   a. Select which activities are appropriate for your student based on
      1) where he is in the Wise List
      2) whether he's a reader
      3) how much writing he can do
      4) whether he's been through the list before
      5) interest and need
   b. He does NOT need to complete every activity for each list each year. Ideally he'll repeat lists and can pick up other activities the second time through (see SWR pg 64).

2. **THEN look for whether there is a worksheet.**
   a. Remember, not all the activities lend themselves to a worksheet, so if you only go by what's in the worksheets, you'll miss some great activities!
   b. There are a few extra pages in the worksheets that you won't find assignments for in *The Wise Guide*. They are marked "Extra" on the Table of Contents and on the lower right corner of these worksheets since there is no corresponding Wise Guide page.

3. **Integrate your lessons to save on time!**
   a. The majority of worksheets start with a quiz. Use this as a followup to new words you just taught (see SWR pg 90, 4.).
   b. Quizzes are an excellent way to reinforce new material, and you have just set up a language activity to complete either now or later in the week — two activities in one!
   c. Schedule the worksheet quiz for when you have just taught the last of that week's list. It is common for an entire list to have been taught in order to use a reinforcement activity.

4. **Immediately correct work** - don't let your student practice errors.
   a. Before moving into the meat of the activity, be sure your student has spelled everything correctly from the quiz.
   b. Have him make the corrections on the page rather than your writing them for him. Re-writing is a valuable part of the learning experience for him. Have him say the phonogram sounds while he writes them.

   > Immediately correct his work. Don't let him practice his errors.

5. **Modify requirements as necessary.**
   a. The worksheets are meant to be a help to you, not dictate how your lessons will necessarily play out.
   b. For example, an assignment may include creating derivatives for all

20 spelling words. You might modify that to require only 10 or 15, if that is more appropriate to your student.

   c. Sentence writing goals can always be adjusted, and some assignments even include a blank at the top of the page in the student's instructions for you to fill in the number of sentences you're requiring of your student.

6. **Use flash cards to teach word-building activities.**
   a. Make a copy of WG pp 98 and 116 for suffix and prefix cards. Cut these apart and tuck them away in an envelope for activities in which your student is creating derivatives.
   b. Build a set of flash cards as you work your way through *The Wise Guide* and keep them organized so you can quickly pull out the cards you need for review words. I used a shoe box and made dividers for the alphabet.
   c. As adults, we understand the process for mixing and rearranging language components, but young ones are *concrete learners*, which means they benefit from physically manipulating the language to understand how we can mix and match or rearrange word parts to create new words.
   d. Once older students understand how to mentally mix and match words and word parts, these flash cards aren't as necessary. However, some students will need them all the time.

7. **Have students practice reading their work, especially sentences.**
   a. The student's Learning Log and these activities make up his first "reader" (see SWR pg 120).
   b. Have him find people he can read his writing to. This strengthens his reading skills and builds excitement for future writing. Writers need an audience!

III. INDEPENDENT WORK vs. GUIDED LEARNING

> The moment you ask the child to complete an assignment independently, it has become a test of what he knows — or doesn't know.

1. When the idea of a worksheet comes to mind, **most teachers think "independent work."**
   a. Regardless of the extent of your instruction on a concept, the moment you ask the child to complete an assignment independently, it has become a "test" of what he knows — or doesn't know — rather than a continuation of your teaching.
   b. You have a lost teaching opportunity when the student makes multiple errors on a worksheet and then just moves on to the next activity. Yes, you can check off that assignment as "completed" and assign a poor grade, but the student either learned next to nothing or will remember incorrect information.
   c. Only use the worksheet as an independent activity if he can do so successfully on his own. That means that completing the worksheet together may be part of your lesson plan.

2. **Teaching vocabulary is a huge part of teaching reading.**
   a. As children grow and mature, their vocabulary needs to develop as well.
   b. A good vocabulary is necessary for strong reading comprehension. A child can have good decoding skills, but if he doesn't know what the words mean, he won't understand what he's reading.

c. Many of the activities are intended to teach and stretch the student's vocabulary.

d. Teachers may find their own vocabulary being stretched. Model for your students a love for learning and get comfortable saying, "Let's look it up!" You're not expected to know it all, and your children will benefit greatly from your example of being willing to learn and grow.

e. This is especially important for teachers who have learned English as a second language. Plan to learn along with your student.

> A good vocabulary is necessary for strong reading comprehension.

3. **Children will need your help** determining if a word they're building is a legitimate English word.

   a. During compound word activities, kids will commonly select common two-word phrases or hyphenated words, which are not real compound words. For example: *makeup* is a compound word but *made up* is a common two-word phrase that includes a verb & preposition.

   b. When adding prefixes or suffixes to base words, kids get the idea of mixing and matching but don't necessarily make legitimate words.

   c. Use a good dictionary or an online resource such as http://dictionary.reference.com or http://www.thefreedictionary.com. Mobile apps are helpful with common words but are often insufficient for the kind of word study you want to do, especially in the later Wise Lists.

IV. An ERRATA Page will be listed on our web site. Let us know if you find something that you think is a typographical error. We'll check it out and add it to the list for others' benefit.

http://www.swrtraining.com/enrichment-activity-worksheets-errata/

Wise Guide
Enrichment Activity
Worksheets

For Multiple
Lists

Date:	Score:
1.	
2.	
3.	
4.	
5.	
6.	
7.	
8.	
9.	
10.	

Date:	Score:
1.	
2.	

Teacher Notes:

1. At the beginning of each day's lesson, the student needs to take a phonogram quiz (see SWR Step #5 & #6, pg 40).

2. Use one of these pages each week and write the Wise List(s) you're currently studying at the top so you can keep track of where the student was during this time.

3. Encourage daily quizzes, rather than quizzing four times on one day.

4. Select phonograms that will be included in that day's dictation, phonograms that need review, or new phonograms the student has recently learned.

5. You can also use this warmup quiz to review words missed on previous spelling tests.

6. Limit your quizzes to 5-10 items each day. Consistent and quick quizzes are an effective way to review these invaluable phonograms.

Date:	Score:
1.	
2.	
3.	
4.	
5.	
6.	
7.	
8.	
9.	
10.	

Date:	Score:
1.	
2.	
3.	
4.	
5.	
6.	
7.	
8.	
9.	
10.	

                                       SWR Steps #5 & #6, pg 40

Time for reading 70 phonograms: _____ seconds

Date:	Score:
1.	
2.	
3.	
4.	
5.	
6.	
7.	
8.	
9.	
10.	

Date:	Score:
1.	
2.	
3.	
4.	
5.	
6.	
7.	
8.	
9.	
10.	

Date:	Score:
1.	
2.	
3.	
4.	
5.	
6.	
7.	
8.	
9.	
10.	

	Score:
9.	
10.	

Teacher Notes:

1. As early as List I-4, you can start timing the student once a week while he reads the phonograms with just their sounds, not the rules or any other phonogram language. For example, for the AY phonogram, he would merely say the sound /A/, not the whole dialogue like he normally does ("AY, the two-letter /A/, that we MAY use at the end of English words").

2. At the beginning of each day's lesson, the student needs to take a phonogram quiz (see SWR Step #5 & #6, pg 40).

3. Use one of these pages each week and write the Wise List(s) you're currently studying at the top so you can keep track of where the student was during this time.

4. Encourage daily quizzes, rather than quizzing four times on one day.

5. Select phonograms that will be included in that day's dictation, phonograms that need review, or new phonograms the student has recently learned.

6. You can also use this warmup quiz to review words missed on previous spelling tests.

7. Limit your quizzes to 5-10 items each day. Consistent and quick quizzes are an effective way to review these invaluable phonograms.

Date _____

1		30		59	
2		31		60	
3		32		61	
4		33		62	
5		34		63	
6		35		64	
7		36		65	
8		37		66	
9					
10					
11					
12					
13					
14					
15					
16					
17					
18					
19					
20					
21		50			
22		51			
23		52			
24		53			
25		54			
26		55			
27		56			
28		57			
29		58			

Teacher Notes:

1. Periodically, you'll want to give your student a quiz on all the phonograms he has learned. Give this quiz at the end of each school quarter for a good assessment of student progress.

2. Print out an extra copy of the student page for this worksheet and label it "Answer Key." Write in the phonograms in the order you're going to dictate them so that you have an answer key that matches that specific quiz. Vary the order of phonograms on each quiz you give.

3. To indicate your student's score, enter the total correct out of how many phonograms you gave on the quiz. For example: 63/70 would mean the student wrote 63 phonograms correctly out of 70 administered.

1		30		59	
2		31		60	
3		32		61	
4		33		62	
5					
6					
7					
8					
9					
10					
11					
12					
13					
14					
15					
16					
17					
18					
19					
20					
21					
22					
23					
24					
25		54		83	
26		55		84	
27		56		85	
28		57		86	
29		58		87	

Teacher Notes:

1. Periodically, you'll want to give your student a quiz on all the phonograms he has learned. Give this quiz at the end of each school quarter for a good assessment of student progress.

2. Print out an extra copy of the student page for this worksheet and label it "Answer Key." Write in the phonograms in the order you're going to dictate them so that you have an answer key that matches that specific quiz. Vary the order of phonograms on each quiz you give.

3. To indicate your student's score, enter the total correct out of how many phonograms you gave on the quiz. For example: 57/74 would mean the student wrote 57 phonograms correctly out of 74 administered (70 basic + 4 advanced phonograms).

4. Once your student has started learning advanced phonograms (SWR Step #38), you can include them on the quiz (see spaces #71-87). Whether you include these phonograms for a grade or just for practice is up to you. However, if you're going to include advanced phonograms on this quiz, be sure you're quizzing them frequently on your daily phonogram quizzes as preparation.

5. Advanced phonogram cards are not required but are helpful for more frequent review once an advanced phonogram has been introduced. See our web site for these cards. www.swrtraining.com

Write & Draw

Teacher Notes:

1. At least once weekly you want your student to be writing sentences or some other directed writing activity.

2. Use this page with a young student in the early lists who is still working on his penmanship.

3. The sentences do not need to be related.

4. Encourage him to choose one of his sentences to illustrate in the space above.

Write & Draw

Teacher Notes:

1. At least once weekly you want your student to be writing sentences or some other directed writing activity.

2. Use this page with a young student who is making progress on his penmanship, as the lines are closer in size to those found in the Learning Log.

3. The sentences do not need to be related.

4. Encourage him to choose one of his sentences to illustrate in the space above.

1. Look at the *Silent Final E Reference Page* in your Learning Log and use it to complete this page.

2. Add the *silent final E* markings to all of the words listed below.

3. Any other markings have already been done for you.

> **Teacher Note:**
> Use this page after teaching the Silent Final E's to reinforce the new rules. This page works best with students who have some reading ability.

cake   glue₂   hinge₃

these   tone   charge₃

dance₃   serve₂   house₅

carve₂   ap ple₄   style

type   tape   pad dle₄

tense₅   fine   val ue₂

gig gle₄   goose₅   splurge₃

1. Take a quiz on 24 spelling words and/or phonograms. Write them in any box you like to mix it up.

2. Correct them to be sure everything is written correctly.

3. As your teacher calls out the words and/or phonograms, cross them out. You can call out "BINGO" every time you get five in a row. Keep going until all your boxes are crossed out.

Teacher Notes:

1. Make copies of this page to pull out when you need a fun change of pace for phonogram or review word review.

2. Include phonograms from a new spelling list you're teaching that day so they're fresh, and the student is ready to use them in new words.

3. For efficient paper usage, put this page in a sheet protector or one of the Quick Response sleeves found at www.swrtraining.com. The student uses a dry erase marker and then simply wipes it clean when he's done.

FREE

⭐

SPOT

1. Take a quiz on 27 phonograms. Write them in any box you like, to mix it up.

2. As your teacher calls out a phonogram, find it and cross it out. Draw a line through every three phonograms that you cross out in a row. Cross out a box when you have all of the phonograms crossed out inside it. When you have all three boxes crossed out, you've got a THREENGO!

Teacher Notes:

1. Make copies of this page to pull out when you need a fun change of pace for phonogram or review word review.

2. Include phonograms from a new spelling list you're teaching that day so they're fresh, and the student is ready to use them in new words.

3. For efficient paper usage, put this page in a sheet protector or one of the Quick Response sleeves found at www.swrtraining.com. The student uses a dry erase marker and then simply wipes it clean when he's done.

1.   Take a quiz on 25 phonograms. Write them in any of the pathway steps you like.

2.   When you use a phonogram in your spelling words, cross it out.

3.   Once you have crossed out all of your pathway steps, you can move from START to FINISH!

START

Teacher Notes:

1. Make copies of this page to pull out when you need a fun change of pace for phonogram or review word review.

2. Include phonograms from a new spelling list you're teaching that day so they're fresh, and the student is ready to use them in new words.

3. After you teach each new spelling word, have the student cross out any of the phonograms used in that word that he wrote on this page.

4. For efficient paper usage, put this page in a sheet protector or one of the Quick Response sleeves found at www.swrtraining.com. The student uses a dry erase marker and then simply wipes it clean when he's done.

FINISH

Wise Guide
Enrichment Activity
Worksheets

Lists A-C

1. Look at a penny. On one side is a picture of President Lincoln. On the other side is a picture of the Lincoln Memorial, which is in Washington, D.C. These sides of the coin are *opposites*.

2. Words can have *opposites* also. For example, *up & down* or *big & little* are *opposites*.

3. Your teacher will read the words in the first column. Which of your spelling words are the *opposites*? Write them in the second column.

4. Are there some left that you're not sure about? Listen as your teacher reads your spelling words to you. Write the last ones.

Opposite	Spelling Word
is not	is
walk	run
come	go
bottom	top
undo	do
none	all
am not	am
your	my
did not	did

                                                                           WG pg 3

1. Look at the picture. One person is *tall* but the other person is *short*. These words are *opposites* or *antonyms.*

2. Your teacher will read the words in the first column. Which of your spelling words are the *opposites*? Write them in the second column.

3. Are there some words that you weren't sure about? Listen as your teacher reads your spelling words to you. Write the last ones.

Antonym	Spelling Word
bad	good
demand	beg
valley	hill
little	big
can't	can
desert	bog
pale skin	tan
normal	odd
first	last
miss (as in baseball)	hit
yes	no
help	bug

1. Take a quiz on some of your spelling words. Correct your quiz.

2. A *compound word* is a word that is made of two base words. For example, *bath + tub = bathtub.*

3. Match your words together to create four *compound words*.

4. Draw pictures of two of these new words in the boxes below. Write the word on the line beneath its picture.

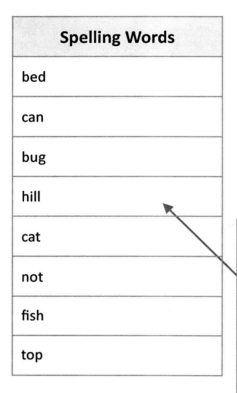

Spelling Words
bed
can
bug
hill
cat
not
fish
top

Compound Words
bedbug
cannot
hilltop
catfish

Teacher Notes:

1. Quiz the student on the words in the "Spelling Words" list.

2. Use flash cards to show the student how to mix and match the words to create different combinations. Have him write his answers in the "Compound Words" chart.

3. Sample illustrations are shown below. The student may choose different words or to illustrate these words differently.

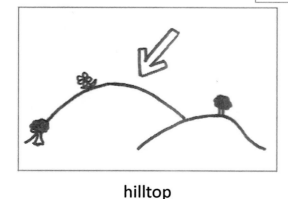

hilltop

catfish

1. Take a quiz on some of your spelling words. Correct your quiz.

2. A *compound words* is a word that is made of two base words. For example, *bath + tub = bathtub*.

3. Match your words together to create five *compound words*.

4. Write two of your *compound words* on the lines at the bottom of the page. Draw pictures of these new words in the boxes.

Spelling Words	
all	over
bed	run
bug	set
do	step
hill	to
in	top
on	up
out	

Compound Words		
bedbug	outset	overstep
hilltop	overall	setup
instep	overalls	uphill
onto	overdo	upon
outdo	overrun	upset

Teacher Notes:
1. Multiple possibilities for compound words are listed, but the student only needs to come up with five.
2. Young students need help understanding how to mix and match words. Use flash cards with the spelling words on them. Show the student how to put two words together, alternating which comes first.
3. Help the student with vocabulary. There are words listed here that he will probably not be familiar with.
4. Identify for him when he creates a legitimate word.

TEACHER NOTE: Sample illustrations are shown below. The student may choose different words to illustrate or to illustrate these words differently.

upset

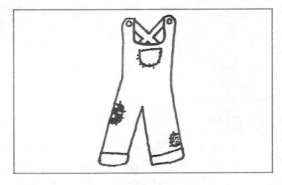

overalls

1. A *pronoun* is a word that is used instead of a *noun* (a person, place, thing, or idea).

> **Tom** sat on the bed.   Tom ran to the **cat**.
> **He** sat on the bed.   Tom ran to **it**.

2. Some of your new spelling words are *pronouns*. Use the sample sentences to fill in the charts below.

_____ can go.

Subject Pronouns		
Person	**Singular**	**Plural**
1st	I	we
2nd	you	you
3rd	he, she, it	they (advanced option)

Tom can run to _____.

Object Pronouns		
Person	**Singular**	**Plural**
1st	me	us
2nd	you	you
3rd	him, her, it	them (advanced option)

Teacher Notes:
1. Just like nouns, pronouns can be *singular* (only one) or *plural* (more than one).

2. Pronouns also communicate *person*, telling us about who is being talked to or about.
> *1st person* - person speaking about himself
> *2nd person* - person being spoken to
> *3rd person* - person being spoken about

3. The words *them* and *they* will be taught in Lists H-2 and I-3, respectively. If your student learned these in a previous year, you can include them now.

Wise Guide
Enrichment Activity
Worksheets

Lists D-F

1. A *noun* is a word that describes a person, a place, a thing, or an idea. You know it's a *noun* when you can put *a, an, the,* or a *number word* in front of it.

     a bug   *an odd cat*   *the mother*   *six cats*

2. Listen as your teacher reads your spelling words to you. What kind of a *noun* is it? Write the word in the correct column below.

Nouns			
Persons	**Places**	**Things**	**Ideas**
man	home	book	time
boy	school	dog	
mother	street	school	
		hand	

Teacher Notes:
1. The first 10 words in List D are all *nouns* (words #61-70).

2. Read these words to your student *in the order found in the WG* and have him categorize them. You purposely want to read them in a scrambled order (not how they're listed above) so that he has to think about what kind of *noun* each would be before writing it.

3. The *noun school* can be used as either a place or as a thing. For example:
       "The boy is at his school now." (place)
             OR
       "The children wanted to do their work for school before lunch." (thing)

   Let your student choose how he wants to categorize this word.

1. Take a quiz on some of your spelling words. Correct your quiz.

2. A **compound word** is a word that is made of two base words. For example, *bed + bug = bedbug*.

3. Mix and match your words to create six **compound words**.

4. Draw pictures of two of these new words in the boxes at the bottom of the page. Write the **compound word** on the line beneath its picture.

Spelling Words	
bag	out
bed	over
book	play
hand	school
home	step
make	time
mother	up

Compound Words	
bedtime	makeup
handbag	outplay
handbook	overhand
handout	overtime
homeschool	stepmother
makeover	

Teacher Notes:
1. Multiple possibilities are listed, but the student only needs to come up with six of these.
2. Sample illustrations are shown below. The student may choose different words to illustrate or to illustrate these words differently.

handbag

bedtime

1. We make *contractions* when we combine two words, remove one or more letters from one of the words, and replace the missing letter(s) with an *apostrophe*.

2. Write the words your teacher dictates below and then write the *contractions* with the *apostrophe*.

  <u>   did   </u> + <u> not </u> = <u>   didn't   </u>   <u> he </u> + <u> is </u> = <u>   he's   </u>

  <u>   is   </u> + <u> not </u> = <u>   isn't   </u>   <u> she </u> + <u> is </u> = <u>   she's   </u>

  <u>   I   </u> + <u> am </u> = <u>   I'm   </u>

> **Teacher Note:** Dictate the words that are in *bold* on the lines and in the chart below. Then guide your student as necessary to complete the contractions.

3. Write some more review words that your teacher tells you.

4. Match the words in each open space to make *contractions*.

	I	you	we	not
are		you're	we're	aren't
had	I'd	you'd	we'd	hadn't
have	I've	you've	we've	haven't
must				mustn't
was				wasn't
has				hasn't

5. Write a sentence using one of your *contractions*.

Answers will vary.

   Example: I didn't go to bed. I've got a cat.

1. One kind of **verb** describes an **action** that you can act out. Other **verbs** that you can't really act out are called **state of being** or **helping verbs.**

    sit   run   hit   *is   am   be*

2. Listen as your teacher reads some of your spelling words to you. Which kind of **verb** is it? Write the word in the correct column below.

3. Choose two **action verbs** and draw a picture of someone performing this action in the boxes below. Write the **verb** under its picture.

Teacher Notes:
1. The second half of List D includes all **verbs** (words #71-80).
2. Read each one to your student and ask...
   - could the word be acted out? (action)
   - could it help another verb? (e.g. "She *must* jump." or "I *have* played.")
   - could it be used to describe someone? (e.g. "She *was* happy." or "They *are* friends.")

Action Verbs	State of Being or Helping Verbs
make	are
jump	must
say	was
play	has
school (optional)	have
	had

play

jump

Teacher Note: The word *school* could be used as a verb as in the sentence, *"The parents will school their own children at home."*

1. Take a quiz on some review words and some current spelling words. Correct your quiz.

2. A *verb* can describe an action.   *sit*   *make*   *play*

3. When we are talking about another person or something that is doing an action, we add *-s* or *-es* to the end of the *verb*.

                                   she sits   *he makes*   *it plays*

4. Practice writing your *verbs* in the correct form to finish the charts.

5. Find two more *verbs* from List D to finish your chart.

> **Teacher Note:** Dictate the words in *bold* to the student. See the instructions on WG pg 12.

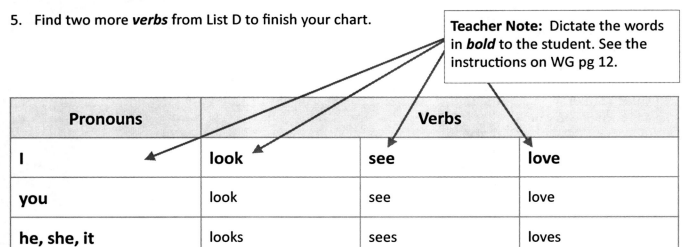

Pronouns	Verbs		
I	**look**	**see**	**love**
you	look	see	love
he, she, it	looks	sees	loves

Pronouns	Verbs		
I	**wave**	**kill**	**like**
you	wave	kill	like
he, she, it	waves	kills	likes

Pronouns	Verbs		
I	**trade**	answers will vary	answers will vary
you	trade	answers will vary	answers will vary
he, she, it	trades	answers will vary	answers will vary

1. Look at the picture. One animal is *big* but the other animal is *small*. These words are *opposites* or *antonyms.*

2. Your teacher will help you read the words in the first column. Which of your spelling words are the *opposites*? Write them in the second column.

3. Are there some left that you're not sure about? Listen as your teacher reads your spelling words to you. Write the last ones.

Opposite	Spelling Word
can't	may
hate	love
heal	kill
overlook	see or look
that	this
dry	wash
long	short
misery	fun
won't	will
dislike	like
adult	baby
tool	toy
thin	thick
sell	trade
my	your

1. Take a quiz on some review words and on some current spelling words. Correct your quiz.

2. A *compound word* is a word that is made of two base words. For example, *hill + top = hilltop*.

3. Mix and match your words to create four *compound words*.

4. Draw pictures of two of these new words in the boxes at the bottom of the page. Write the *compound word* on the line beneath its picture.

Spelling Words	
be	over
home	see
like	short
look	trade
man	wash
may	wave
out	

Compound Words	
homelike	oversee
lookout	shortwave
maybe	tradesman
overlook	washout

Teacher Notes:
1. Multiple possibilities are listed, but the student only needs to come up with four of these.
2. Sample illustrations are shown below. The student may choose different words to illustrate or to illustrate these words differently.

lookout

tradesman

1. We make *contractions* when we combine two words, remove one or more letters from one of the words, and replace the missing letter(s) with an *apostrophe*.

2. Write the words your teacher dictates below and then write the *contractions* with the *apostrophe*.

Teacher Note: Dictate the words in *bold* and then guide your student as necessary to complete the contractions.

	will
I	I'll
you	you'll
he	he'll
she	she'll
it	it'll
we	we'll

3. Write a sentence using one of your *contractions.*

Answers will vary.

Examples: I'll be home at six.

She'll go to school.

1. Every syllable must have a *vowel*. These *vowels* might be spelled with a single letter or with a multi-letter phonogram.

2. As you take your quiz, think about the *vowel* in the word. If it is spelled with a single letter, is the *vowel* saying its first, second, or third sound? Is it spelled with a multi-letter phonogram? Write the words in the correct columns below.

3. Correct your quiz.

Single-letter Vowels		
1st sound	2nd sound	3rd sound
little	old	wall
hot	cold	
long	ice	
flat	wild	
milk	child	
shot		
land		

> **Teacher Note:**
> Read the List F words to your student *in the order found in the WG* and have him categorize them. You purposely want to read them in a scrambled order (not how they're listed on this sheet) so that he has to think about the word and how its *vowel sound* is spelled before writing it.

Multi-Letter Phonogram Vowels		
green	star	floor
sea	day	
bread	hair	

1. A **noun** is a word for a person, a place, a thing, or an idea. An **adjective** is a word that describes a **noun**.

    mother   house   bed   love   *red   six   the   a*

2. Take a quiz on words from List F. Write the words that could be **adjectives** in the first column and those that can be **nouns** in the second column. Some words could be both an **adjective** and a **noun**.

3. Correct your work to be sure everything is spelled correctly.

4. In the last column, use your **adjectives** to describe the **nouns** by writing **noun phrases**. You can mix and match to find different combinations as you like.

Adjectives	Nouns	Adjectives + Nouns
old	bread	answers will vary
little	child	Examples: old bread, ice milk, green hair
hot	star	**Teacher Notes:**
cold	day	1. The first 10 words in List F can be used as **adjectives** while the second 10 words are **nouns.** Some words could be both.
green	wall	
ice	milk	2. To help your student think carefully about the part of speech for these words, **dictate them in the order listed below,** which will result in his writing them as listed on this answer key to the left.
long	cold	
sea	ice	
wild	hair	1. old 11. green
		2. little 12. ice
flat	sea	3. bread 13. long
		4. hot 14. hair
	floor	5. child 15. sea
		6. star 16. wild
	land	7. day 17. floor
		8. wall 18. land
	flat	9. milk 19. flat
		10. cold 20. shot
	shot	3. The following words are listed in both categories: *cold, ice, sea,* and *flat.*

1. Look at a penny. On one side is a picture of President Lincoln. On the other side is a picture of the Lincoln Memorial in Washington D.C. These sides of the coin are *opposites.*

2. Your teacher will help you read the words in the first column. Which of your spelling words are the *opposites*? Write them in the second column.

3. Are there some left that you're not sure about? Listen as your teacher reads your spelling words to you. Write the last ones.

Opposite	Spelling Word
young	old
sea	land
night	day
tame	wild
hot	cold
big	little or short
adult	child
short	long
steam	ice
ceiling	floor
bumpy	flat

1. We have five *senses* to understand the world around us. They help us *see, hear, taste, feel,* and *smell.*

2. *Adjectives* are words that describe *nouns* and can describe what we are *sensing.*

    stinky fish (smell)   *soft dog* (feel)   *loud pop* (hear)

3. As your teacher reads your spelling words, think about whether that *adjective* could be used to describe a "thing" which you could *see*. Write the *adjective* in that column. Repeat for each *sense.*

4. Some of the *adjectives* can be used in different ways and you would use different *senses*, so you may need to write the words more than one time. For example, *flat* could describe a *pancake* (see), a *note* someone sings (hear), *soda* you're drinking (taste), or the top of a table (feel and/or see).

5. At the bottom of the page, draw pictures using two of these *adjectives* to describe a *noun*. Write the *adjective* & *noun* combination on the line beneath your picture.

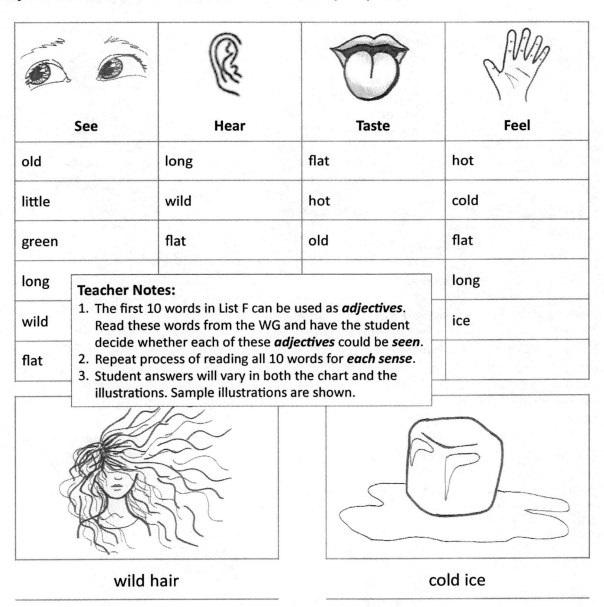

See	Hear	Taste	Feel
old	long	flat	hot
little	wild	hot	cold
green	flat	old	flat
long			long
wild			ice
flat			

> **Teacher Notes:**
> 1. The first 10 words in List F can be used as *adjectives*. Read these words from the WG and have the student decide whether each of these *adjectives* could be *seen*.
> 2. Repeat process of reading all 10 words for *each sense*.
> 3. Student answers will vary in both the chart and the illustrations. Sample illustrations are shown.

wild hair   cold ice

1. Take a quiz on some review words and on some of your spelling words. Correct your quiz.

2. A *compound words* is a word that is made of two *base words*. For example, *cow + boy = cowboy.*

3. Match your review words together with your spelling words to create one *compound word* for each new spelling word.

4. Draw pictures of two of these new words in the boxes. Write the *compound word* on the line beneath its picture.

> **Teacher Notes:** Sample illustrations are shown below. The student may choose different words or to illustrate these words differently.

Review Words	
bed	in
cat	like
do	mother
fish	over
home	up

starfish

Spelling Words	Compound Words
hot	hotbed, hotshot
wild	wildcat
sea	seabed
child	childlike
star	starfish
hair	hairdo
shot	overshot, upshot
land	homeland, inland, motherland, overland

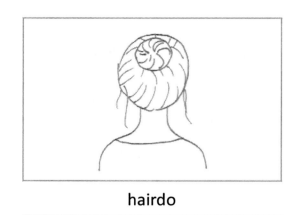

hairdo

Wise Guide
Enrichment Activity
Worksheets

Lists G-H

1. Take a quiz on some review words and on some of your new spelling words.

2. Correct your quiz so that everything is spelled correctly.

3. Combine your spelling words with the review words to create one *compound word* for each spelling word.

4. Sometimes you'll need to add a suffix like *-ing* or *-s* to make a *compound word*.

Review Words		
a	in	out
ice	man	steps
	over	

Spelling Word	Compound Word
let	inlet
door	indoors, doorman, outdoors, doorsteps
live	alive, outlive
heat	overheat
box	icebox
stand	outstanding
come	income, overcome

1. There are some words that "go together" because they are expressions or they are frequently used together. Here are some examples.

   sink or swim   *pen and ink*
   jam and bread   *peanut butter and jelly*

2. If you are able, read the word on each line, or listen as your teacher reads it to you. Think of the word from List G that completes this word pair and write it in the same line in the open space.

live	**die**
window	door
read	**write**
yes	**no**
now	**then**
for	**against**
stand	**sit**
ask	**answer**
bacon	**eggs**
dead	live

> **Teacher Note:** Words in **bold** are the words already provided for the student.

1. A **noun** is a word that describes a person, a place, a thing, or an idea. You know it's a **noun** when you can put **a, an, the,** or a **number word** in front of it.

    a bug   *an ill dog*   *the mother*   *six cats*

2. Find words in your Learning Log from Lists E-G that could be **nouns** and write them in the correct columns below.

Persons		Places		Ideas	
baby	E	sea	F	love	E
child	F	flat	F	fun	E
		star	F	trade	E
		wall	F	day	F
		floor	F		
		land	F		
		lot (as in "vacant lot")	G		

Teacher Note: Some students may want to categorize words differently. For example, a *wall* is a **place** for a spider but it's a **thing** that a person can bump into. Likewise, the *sea* is a **thing** we see on a map, but it's a **place** where we sail a boat. Let the student choose the categories.

Teacher Note: The Wise List where each noun is found is indicated for the teacher. The student does **not** need to make note of this information.

Things					
look	E	flat	F	gas	G
wave	E	bread	F	door	G
ring	E	star	F	lot (collective noun)	G
toy	E	wall	F	bacon	G
robe	E	milk	F	heat	G
wash	E	hair	F	box	G
ice	F	shot	F	stand	G
sea	F	floor	F	wing	G

1. The words *a* and *an* are used before a *noun* or before an *adjective* that is describing a *noun*.

    a bed   *a* cat   *an* odd bug   *a* good pet

2. The word *a* is used before a *consonant sound* while the word *an* is used before a *vowel sound*.

3. As your teacher helps you read the words below, listen for the first *sound* in each word. Write *a* or *an*, depending on which *sound* you hear.

a	top	a	big bog
a	short hat	a	red fish
a	red bed	an	old robe
an	odd cat	a	flat wall
a	tan bag	a	little dog
a	hill	a	fun toy
a	ring	an	ice fish
a	street	a	hand

1. An *analogy* is a comparison between two things.

2. Look at the first pair of words and figure out the relationship between them. Then look at the second set of words. They share the same relationship as the first two.

> <u>Red</u> is to <u>strawberry</u> as <u>yellow</u> is to _____lemon or banana_____.

> In this example, the comparison (or the relationship) is fruit color.

3. Below are pairs of words. The first pair relate to one another in some way. How are these words related? Use that same relationship to complete the second pair.

4. Use your spelling words from this week's list to complete each set of *analogies*.

<u>Poor</u> is to <u>rich</u> as <u>little</u> is to _____much_____.

<u>Fans</u> are to the football <u>team</u> as <u>most</u> are to _____some_____.

<u>Glass</u> is to <u>smooth</u> as <u>towel</u> is to _____soft_____.

<u>Contestants</u> are to <u>winner</u> as <u>many</u> is to _____one_____.

<u>Day</u> is to <u>week</u> as <u>month</u> is to _____year_____.

<u>Car</u> is to <u>garage</u> as <u>family</u> is to _____house_____.

<u>Lady</u> is to <u>man</u> as <u>hers</u> is to _____his_____.

<u>Thirst</u> is to <u>water</u> as <u>hunger</u> is to _____food_____.

<u>Dime</u> is to <u>ten</u> as <u>nickel</u> is to _____five_____.

1. Take a quiz on some review words and on some of your spelling words. Correct your quiz.

2. A *compound words* is a word that is made of two base words. For example, *star + fish = starfish.*

3. Match your review words together with your spelling words to create one *compound word* for each spelling word.

Review Words		
as	door	play
book	hand	sea
by	in	three
day	out	top
	over	

Spelling Words	Compound Words
much	inasmuch, overmuch
ball	handball, softball
law	outlaw, bylaw
lay	inlay, layover, layout, outlay, overlay
soft	softball
path	pathway
lone	lonesome
food	seafood
year	yearbook
house	outhouse, housetop, playhouse
way	away, byway, doorway, layaway
some	someday, someway, threesome

1. An *analogy* is a comparison between two things.

2. Look at the first pair of words and figure out the relationship between them. Then look at the second set of words. They share the same relationship as the first two.

    Red is to strawberry as yellow is to _____lemon or banana_____ .

    In this example, the comparison (or the relationship) is fruit color.

3. Below are pairs of words. The first pair relate to one another in some way. How are these words related? Use that same relationship to complete the second pair.

4. Use your spelling words from this week's list to complete each set of *analogies*.

Here is to there as this is to _____that_____.

Morning is to midnight as early is to _____late_____.

Man is to child as high is to _____low_____.

Play is to game as bite is to _____apple_____.

1. A **noun** is a word that describes a person, a place, a thing, or an idea. You know it's a **noun** when you can put **a, an, the,** or a number word in front of it.

    a bug   *the mother*   *six cats*

2. Listen as your teacher reads words from List H-2. If the word can be used as a **noun**, write it in the appropriate column. If the word is not a **noun**, write it in the "Not Nouns" section.

3. Correct your work.

Nouns			
Persons	**Places**	**Things**	**Ideas**
men	yard	row	call
		salt	bite
		coat	yard
		apple	
		well	

Not Nouns			
belong	bring	get	send
tell	how	low	other
late	that	them	

Teacher Note: Read the List H-2 words to your student *in the order found in the WG.* You purposely want to read them in a scrambled order (not how they're listed on this worksheet) so that your student has to think about whether the word can be used as a noun and, if so, what category of noun it is.

1. In the first column, take a quiz on some review words and on some of your new spelling words. Correct your work so that everything is spelled correctly.

2. The words you wrote are *action verbs,* meaning that they describe actions or what someone does.

3. *Verbs* also tell us *when* something happens, happened, or will happen. This is called *tense.* The *verbs* you wrote are in *present tense*, meaning it is something that happens regularly.

    I *sleep* in my bed.   I *eat* my food.   I *play* with the cat.

4. Practice adding the *ED ending* to your *verbs* to make them *past tense*. Write the new word in the correct column. Some of the *verbs* don't use this ending because they are *irregular*. Can you find them?

Present Tense	ed	2 ed	3 ed	X
land	landed			
heat	heated			
play		played		
jump			jumped	
run				ran
do				did
hit				hit
have				had
call		called		
row		rowed		
salt	salted			
belong		belonged		
bring				brought
bite				bit
get				got
send				sent
coat	coated			
tell				told

Teacher Notes:
1. These irregular verbs will be taught later in the Wise List but are needed to complete this page. Help your student with these new words as needed.
2. If your student learned the OUGH phonogram in a previous year, you can teach *brought* now. Otherwise you can chose:
   (a) use kiss-kissed instead of bring-brought,
   (b) introduce OUGH now & use *brought*, or
   (c) wait until List I-1 to finish this page.

Wise Guide
Enrichment Activity
Worksheets

Lists I-1 to I-4

1. Take a quiz on some of your review words and on some new spelling words in the first column.

2. Correct your work.

3. The words you wrote are all *nouns*. One of the ways we know a word is a *noun* is that it can show *possession*, meaning that we can show that something belongs to it. We show possession with *nouns* by adding an *apostrophe* and *-s*. Here are some *possessive nouns* and the "thing" they could each possess.

   boy's toy   *child's cat*   *toy's top*

4. *Pronouns* take the place of *nouns*. They can show *possession* also, but they don't use the *apostrophe* and *-s* ending.

   his toy   *her cat*   *its top*

5. Practice changing each of your *nouns* into a *possessive noun* in the second column, and then write the *possessive pronoun* in the third column.

Nouns	Possessive Nouns	Possessive Pronouns
man	man's	his
box	box's	its
mother	mother's	her
cat	cat's	his, her, or its
child	child's	his, her, or its
door	door's	its
pet	pet's	his, her, or its
path	path's	its
food	food's	its
coat	coat's	its
yard	yard's	its
paper	paper's	its
thing	thing's	its

Teacher Notes:

1. People and animals can be male and female. For *non-specific nouns* (e.g. *child* or *cat*) and for *pronouns* representing these *nouns*, the *gender* may or may not be known. For example, we can say the *cat's paw*, but without knowing the cat's *gender*, we could say *his paw*, *her paw*, or even *its paw*. Let the student choose the gender he wants to assign for these *nonspecific nouns*.

2. Differentiate for your student between the possessive pronoun *its* vs. *it's*, a *contraction* that means *it is*.

1. Take a quiz on some review words and on some of your spelling words. Correct your quiz.

2. A *compound words* is a word that is made of two *base words*. For example, *soft + ball = softball.*

3. Match your review words together with your spelling words to create one *compound word* for each new spelling word.

Review Words		
ball	hand	step
bed	home	wall
boy	man	wash
bread	no	way
door	out	yard
	some	

Spelling Words	Compound Words
back	backhand, backyard, backdoor
roll	bedroll
free	freehand, freeman, freeway
foot	football, footstep
sick	homesick, sickbed
thing	nothing, something
page	pageboy
paper	paperback, wallpaper
show	showbread, noshow
stone	stonewall
white	whitewash

1. There are some words that "go together" because they are expressions or they are frequently used together. Here are some examples.

sink or swim   pen and ink
jam and bread   peanut butter and jelly

2. If you are able, read the word on each line, or listen as your teacher reads it to you. Think of the word from List I-1 that completes this word pair and write it in the open space.

Teacher Note: Words in **bold** are the words already provided for the student.		
	hide	show
	black	white
	pencil	paper
	hand	foot
	gave	**took**
	before	after
	healthy	sick
	sing	dance
	enslaved	free
	front	back
	rock	stone
	cut	**glue**
	lift	**drop**
	drop	roll

1. In the first column, take a quiz on some of your new spelling words. Correct your work so that everything is spelled correctly.

2. The words you wrote are *action verbs,* meaning that they describe actions or what someone does.

3. *Verbs* also tell us *when* something happens, happened, or will happen. This is called *tense.* The *verbs* you wrote are in *present tense*, meaning it is something that happens regularly.

>   I *sleep* in my bed.   I *eat* my food.   I *play* with the cat.

4. Practice adding the *ED ending* to your *verbs* to make them *past tense*. Write the new word in the correct column. Some of the *verbs* don't use this ending because they are *irregular.* Can you find them?

Present Tense	ed	ed [2]	ed [3]	X
paper		papered		
lift	lifted			
thank			thanked	
show		showed		
roll		rolled		
cut				cut
give				gave

Bonus				
stone		stoned		
page		paged		
dance			danced	

Teacher Notes:
1. The "bonus" words should be assigned only if the student has been introduced to the E's Dropping Rule (#16) by this time.
2. If you haven't taught that yet, you could dictate the following review words as a bonus: *ask - asked* (3rd sound)
    kill - killed (2nd sound)
    bread - breaded (1st sound)

3. Use this page if your student is using the Primary Learning Log.
4. Black Log users simply add these words to B19 & B20.

Teacher Note: Sample illustrations are shown below. See WG pg 28 for more on this assignment.

winter

spring

summer

fall

1. Take a quiz on some review words and on this week's spelling words.

2. Correct your quiz so that everything is spelled correctly.

3. Add review words to your spelling words to create *compound words*.
   Example: *bull + dog = bulldog*

4. Combine one of the review words with the spelling word you wrote on the last line to form a *contraction*.

Review Words		
less	in	over
like	is	time
	out	

Spelling Word	Compound Word
blow	blowout
put	input, output
take	intake, overtake, takeout, takeover
moon	moonless, moonlike
tree	treeless
spring	springtime, springlike
winter	wintertime, winterlike
summer	summertime, summerlike

Spelling Word	Contraction
what	what's

1. Take a quiz on some of your spelling words. Correct your quiz so that everything is spelled correctly.

2. A *prefix* is a word part that is added to the beginning of a *base word*.

    For example: **re**do **un**do   What is the base word? ___do___   What are the prefixes? ___re-___ ___un-___

3. A *suffix* is a word part added at the end of the word.

    For example: do**ing** ask**ing**   What are the base words? ___do___ ___ask___   The suffix? ___-ing___

4. The *dash* shows where the *base word* would be connected to the *prefix* or *suffix*.
    For example: re-   un-   -ing   Add *dashes* to your *prefixes* and *suffixes* above.

5. These word parts change the meaning of the new word. When we know the meaning of the *base word*, the *prefix,* and the *suffix,* we can know what the new word means!

6. The *prefix mid-* means "middle of." Add that to the first three words in the chart below. What do these new words mean?

7. The *suffix -y* means "characterized by" or it tells what something or someone is like. Add this *suffix* to four of your words in the chart below. What do these new words mean?

Spelling Word	mid-	-y
summer	midsummer	summery
winter	midwinter	wintery
season	midseason	
spring		springy
storm		stormy

8. Write a sentence using one of these new words.

Answers will vary.

     Example: It's cold at midwinter.

Teacher Note:
Be sure the spelling words are dictated in the correct order so that the open spaces for the derivatives will line up correctly for the student.

1. Take a quiz on some of your spelling words. Correct your quiz so that everything is spelled correctly.

Spelling Words		
a.	fish	corn	apples
b.	winter	spring	summer

2. ***Punctuation marks*** tell the reader to start, to stop, to slow down, and to pause. They are used to help make the meaning of our sentences more clear.

3. One reason for a ***comma*** is for making a list.   *I saw a man, a boy, and my mother.*

4. We use a ***colon*** when the introduction to our list could be a complete sentence.
    There are three people I see: a man, a boy, and my mother.

5. Draw an line from the name on the left to the ***punctuation marks*** on the right.

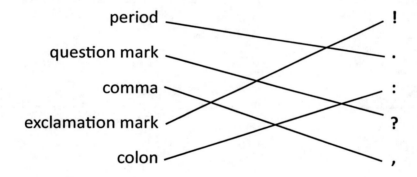

6. Using the two lists on rows a. and b. above, write two sentences that include a ***colon*** and a series of ***commas***. Make sure the introduction to your list *could* stand alone as a complete sentence. Use correct punctuation.

Answers will vary. Examples could include:

For dinner I will cook three foods: fish, corn, and apples.

We can have storms in three seasons: winter, spring, or summer.

> **Teacher Note:** Notice in these examples that the part of the sentence that is before the colon and that introduces the list could be a sentence on its own. Following are ***incorrect*** uses of the colon.   *Three foods that I cook: fish, corn, and apples.*
> *Storms are in: winter, spring, or summer.*

1. Read these sentences.   *Mother got something. Mother read a book. Listen to Mother.*
                                 Do you hear Mother reading? Thank you, Mother.

2. Saying "Mother" over and over and over can get tiring, so we use **pronouns** instead. Doesn't this sound better?
                                 Mother got something. She read a book. Listen to her.
                                 Do you hear her reading? Thank you, Mother.

3. Use the sample sentences to fill in the Pronoun chart below.

_____ *will run.*   *Tom saw _____.*

Singular			
Person		**Subject**	**Object**
	1st	I	me
	2nd	you	you
3rd	M	he	him
	F	she	her
	N	it	it

Plural		
Person	**Subject**	**Object**
1st	we	us
2nd	you	you
3rd	they (advanced option)	them (advanced option)

Teacher Note: *Pronouns* tell us four things about the noun they're replacing.

a. **Person:** 1st person - person speaking
                2nd person - person being spoken to
                3rd person - person being spoken about

b. **Gender:** Masculine (males)   *(Only 3rd person*
                Feminine (females)   *singular pronouns*
                Neuter (neither one)   *use gender.)*

c. **Number:** singular (one)
                plural (more than one)

d. **Case:** subject - person/thing
                          doing the action
              object - person/thing
                          receiving the action

1. Take a quiz on your spelling words. Correct your quiz so that everything is spelled correctly.
2. Sometimes we use little words called *pronouns* instead of a person's name.
   - If the person is the one doing the action, we use **subject pronouns**. <u>Mother</u> got up. <u>She</u> got up.
   - If the person is receiving the action, we use **object pronouns**. Give <u>Dad</u> a hug. Give <u>him</u> a hug.
3. Listen as your teacher reads some sentences with your spelling words. Change the *nouns* to the appropriate *pronouns* and write those in the correct space on the list below.
4. If the *pronoun* is at the beginning of a sentence, be sure to capitalize it.

Spelling Word	1st Pronoun	2nd Pronoun
sing	Him*	He*
sang	He	us
sung	She	her
song	him	it
doll	Her	his
feet	**They**	**it**
zoo	He*	them
miss	She	it
add	We	it
lace	She	her
Mr.	He	Him*
finds	he	it
nice	She	us
plant	He	it
got	We	her
away	**she**	**they**
came	**They**	**His**
west	**They**	**them**
went	She	him
lake	We	it

Teacher Notes:
1. Read sentences from WG pg 30 for this assignment.
2. Younger students may only complete half of this assignment.
3. The word *they* will not be taught until List K-7. You can **(1)** teach that word now and use all the spelling words and their related pronouns, **OR (2)** skip the spelling words and their related pronouns that use *they* (marked in **bold** on this answer key), which means you will not use the last four lines of this assignment.
4. Capitalize pronouns that refer to deity.*

1. In the first column, take a quiz on some review words and on some of your new spelling words.

2. Correct your work so that everything is spelled correctly.

3. The words you wrote are **action verbs,** meaning that they describe actions or what someone does.

4. **Verbs** also tell us **when** something happens, happened, or will happen. This is called **tense.** The **verbs** you wrote are in **present tense**, meaning it is something that happens regularly.

   I *sleep* in my bed.   I *eat* my food.   I *play* with the cat.

5. Practice adding the **ED ending** to your **verbs** to make them **past tense.** Write the new word in the correct column. Some of the **verbs** don't use this ending because they are **irregular**. Can you find them?

Present Tense	ed	²ed	³ed	X
sing				sang
miss			missed	
add	added			
lace			laced	
plant	planted			
find				**found**
get				got
come				came
go				went

Teacher Notes:
1. Use this page if your student is using the Primary Learning Log.
2. Black Log users simply add these words to B19 & B20.

3. The irregular verb *found* won't be taught until List J-4 but is needed to complete this page. Help your student with this new word now.

1. Take a quiz in the first column by writing the simple sentences your teacher dictates to you. They will include a *pronoun* and *verb*.

2. Correct your quiz.

3. *Verbs* tell us *when* something happens (*present*), happened (*past*), or will happen (*future*). This is called *tense.* Each of the *verbs* you wrote for your quiz were in *present tense.*

4. Write each sentence again two times but change the *verb* to *past tense* and *future tense.*

Present Tense Verb	Past Tense Verb	Future Tense Verb
I sing.	I sang.	I will sing.
I miss.	I missed.	I will miss.
I add.	I added.	I will add.
I lace.	I laced.	I will lace.
I plant.	I planted.	I will plant.
I find.	I found.	I will find.
I get.	I got.	I will get.
I come.	I came.	I will come.
I go.	I went.	I will go.

Teacher Note: Dictate the sentences in the first column for the quiz. After it is corrected, the student can finish the other two columns independently, unless he needs your assistance to do so.

1. Take a quiz on some of your spelling words. Correct your quiz so that everything is spelled correctly.

2. A *prefix* is a word part that is added to the beginning of a *base word*.

    For example: undo   What is the prefix? ___un-___   What is the base word? ___do___

3. The *prefix un-* means "not" or the "reverse" of something.

4. Add the *prefix un-* to as many of the words below as you can to make real English words. You might also need to add a *suffix* to two of your words to make a real word.

5. What do these new words mean?

Spelling Word	un-
soon	
very	
zip	unzip
sold	unsold
told	untold
nine	
spent	unspent
form	unformed
end	unending

Teacher Notes:
1. Many young children understand that we add *prefixes* to the beginning of words, like a puzzle piece is added to the puzzle. However, they don't necessarily have the vocabulary to know when adding a *prefix* will actually form a real English word.
2. Help your student navigate through the spelling words to choose those that can use the *un-* prefix, since not all the words can.

6. Write a sentence using one of these new words.

    Answers will vary.

        Example: His song is unending.

1. Take a quiz on some of this week's words in the first column below.

2. Correct your quiz so that everything is spelled correctly.

3. We use *adjectives* to describe *nouns*, and we add the *suffixes -er* or *-est* to an adjective when we are *comparing* nouns.

Suffix	Meaning	Comparison	Jill is tall.
-er	more than	comparing two nouns	Jim is *taller* than Jill.
-est	the most	comparing three or more nouns	Tom is the *tallest* of all.

4. Add the *suffixes -er* and *-est* to each word to create *derivatives* that express *comparison*. The base word actually changes on one of your words. Can you find it?

Positive Degree Spelling Word - Adjective	Comparative Degree "more than" with *-er*	Superlative Degree the "most" with *-est*
rich	richer	richest
new	newer	newest
soon	sooner	soonest
far	farther	farthest
dear	dearer	dearest
good	better	best

Teacher Notes:
1. For the comparative and superlative forms of *far*, we add the voiced TH and then the suffix.

2. The comparisons for *good* are an exception to this general comparison rule (*better* and *best*).

5. Write a sentence using one of your *comparative* or *superlative adjectives*.

Answers will vary.

Example: I went farther down the path than the other boy.

64

Wise Guide
Enrichment Activity
Worksheets

Lists J-1 to J-6

1. Take a quiz on some new spelling words and on some review words.

2. Correct your quiz so that everything is spelled correctly.

3. Add your spelling words to the review words to create *compound words.*

4. Write a sentence using one of your new *compound words*.

Spelling Words			
every	with	daddy	under
son	word	life	lord

Review Words	Compound Word
after	afterlife
by	byword
cut	undercut
dog	underdog
foot	underfoot
go	undergo
hand	underhand
lay	underlay
like	lifelike
long	lifelong

Review Words	Compound Word
one	everyone
over	overlord
shot	undershot
stand	withstand, understand
step	stepson, stepdaddy
take	undertake
thing	everything
time	lifetime
went	underwent

Teacher Notes:
1. Young students need help understanding how to mix and match words. Use flash cards with the spelling words on them. Show the student how to put two words together, alternating their arrangement.
2. Help the student with vocabulary. There are words listed here that he will probably not be familiar with. Identify for him when he creates a legitimate word.

Answers will vary.

        Example: Daddy will undertake a new job.

1. Take a quiz on some review words and on some of this week's spelling words.

2. Correct your quiz so that everything is spelled correctly.

3. All of these words are *prepositions*, which tell how one thing relates to something else.

4. Find three *prepositions* in your List J-2 words and add them to the list.

5. Write two sentences using *prepositions* from your list below.

Prepositions			
in	up	of	down
by	on	like	with
out	onto	for	**from**
to	over	about	**outside**
into	at	after	**inside**

Answers will vary.

    Examples: His arm is in a cast.

              He came from the ship.

Teacher Notes:
1. Use this page if your student is using the Primary Learning Log.
2. Black Log users simply add these words to B30.
3. *Do NOT* dictate the words in **bold** above. These are the *prepositions* the student is to find in his log from List J-2.

1. Take a quiz on some review words, some of this week's spelling words, and a new word.

2. Correct your quiz so that everything is spelled correctly.

3. Either mix and match your spelling words or add review words to them to create a *compound word.*

Review Words			
after	down	man	tan
away	fish	out	under
bed	hill	over	up
by	life	set	pig

Teacher Note: New word not yet taught; teach it now.

Spelling Word	Compound Word
side	bedside, hillside, sideline, outside, upside
oil	oilskin
hard	hardship
noon	afternoon
most	upmost
hang	hangover, hangout, hangman
cast	outcast, downcast, castaway
line	lifeline, underline, fishline
post	outpost, postman
arm	overarm, underarm
skin	oilskin, pigskin
ship	hardship
here	hereafter, hereby, herein
sun	sundown, sunfish, sunset, suntan
age	overage, underage
cover	undercover
mine	undermine

1. Choose six spelling words that could be a *noun* AND a *verb*, and write them on the lines below.

2. Illustrate both the *noun* AND the *verb* for that word in each box. Sometimes this can be a single picture whereas other times you'll need to draw two pictures.

Teacher Note: Sample illustrations are shown below. The student may choose different words or to illustrate these words differently.

group

bill

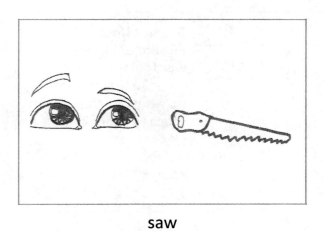

saw

pay

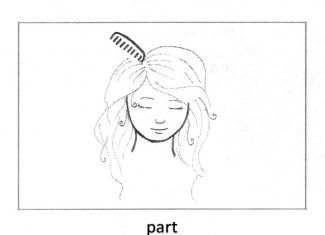

part

wind

1. Take a quiz on two review words and on some of your List J-3 spelling words.

2. Correct your quiz so that everything is spelled correctly.

3. Combine your spelling words with the review words and with *suffixes* to create one *compound word* and/or one *derivative* for each spelling word.

4. Write a sentence using one of your *compound words* or *derivatives*.

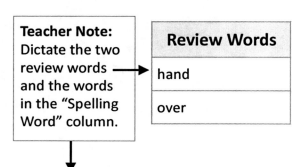

Review Words
hand
over

Suffixes	
-less	without
-ful	full of
-ment	act or state of

Teacher Note: Dictate the two review words and the words in the "Spelling Word" column.

Spelling Word	Compound Word	Derivative
saw	handsaw	**Teacher Note:** Be sure to dictate the words in the correct order so that they line up with available spaces on the page.
bill	handbill	
print	handprint	
left	leftover	
fill	overfill	
pay	overpay	payment
force		forceful
hope		hopeless, hopeful
place		placement
shape		shapeless

Answers will vary.

   Examples: She will take the handbill from him.

            Did she overpay for her dinner?

1. Take a quiz on some review words in the top chart and on some *verbs* from Lists J-1 to J-3 in the second chart.

2. Correct your quiz so that everything is spelled correctly.

3. *Helping verbs* are little words that we use with *verbs* to give them more exact meaning or to change the *tense*.

4. Mix and match the *helping verbs* with the *main verbs* to create your own *verb phrases*.

Helping Verbs	Meaning
can	able to do so
may	permission to OR the possibility of doing so in the future
will	determined to do so in the future
must	required to do so
did	completed in the past

Teacher Note:
Make sure when dictating the helping verbs that the student writes them on the same line as their definitions.

Verbs		Verb Phrase
forget	J-1	Answers will vary.
cover	J-2	Examples: can forget, will cover, must pay, etc.
force	J-3	
dust	J-3	
print	J-3	
pay	J-3	
hope	J-3 ←	
race	J-3	
perch	J-3	
place	J-3	

Teacher Notes:
1. The helping verbs above are all review words.

2. The words in the "Verbs" column come from Wise Lists J-1 to J-3, as noted for the teacher.

1. Write _____ sentences using **verb phrases** that you created on the Helping Verbs worksheet.

2. Include a **prepositional phrase** in each sentence. Look at your **prepositions** list for ideas.

3. Use a capital letter at the beginning and an end mark for each sentence.

4. Underline your **prepositional phrases** and (circle) your **verb phrases**.

Answers will vary. Here are some examples.

I (will pay) my bill for the fudge.

He (can win) the race on Saturday.

The boy (must place) the white shape in the white group.

Teacher Notes:
1. Determine how many sentences you would like your student to write and fill that number in the blank for #1.

2. A *prepositional phrase* includes the *preposition* (P) and the *noun* (N) or *pronoun* (PN) that follows it.

   Example: to Peter   for him
                  P   N   P   PN

3. A *prepositional phrase* might include an entire *noun phrase* (NP), which includes the *noun* any words that describe it.
   Example: to the busy store   for my wonderful mother
                  P   NP   P   NP

4. For this assignment, the student needs to underline the entire *prepositional phrase*. The examples above include these *prepositional phrases*.

   for the fudge
   on Saturday
   in the white group

5. The word *to* is a *preposition* when it is followed by a *noun*, a *noun phrase, or a pronoun.* However, it is part of a *verb phrase* when it is followed by a *verb.*

Prepositional Phrases	Verb Phrases
to the store	to go
to her mom	to eat
to him	to have

1. Take a quiz on some of your spelling words. Correct your work.

2. All of these words are *nouns*, which means they can be more than one or *plural*.

3. Write the *plural* form of each *noun* in the second column.

Single Noun	Plural Noun
sister	sisters
card	cards
bird	birds
fool	fools
inch	inches
supper	suppers
grain	grains
game	games
spur	spurs
role	roles

4. Write a sentence using one of these *plural nouns*.

Answers will vary.

      Examples: We will fun play games all day.

                We will give Mother cards on Mother's Day.

1. Good writers play with language to make it more interesting and fun for the reader.

2. One technique you can add to your writing is called *alliteration,* which is where a *sound* is repeated at the beginning of several words of a sentence. Read this sentence and listen for the *sound* that is repeated.   *The cat called for her kittens when they cried for milk.*

3. As your teacher reads your spelling words, listen to the first *sound* of each word. Does it start with one of the *sounds* below? If so, write it under the appropriate *sound*. (The letter inside the slashes indicates a *sound*.)

/s/	/f/	/b/	/g/
seven	funny	blue	gallon
sisters	found	bird	gold
supper	forgot		grand
spur	fools		grain
			game

4. Write two sentences that include *alliteration,* using some of the words above. Each sentence needs to include <u>at least two</u> of these spelling words, but you're free to add more words to really saturate the sentence with your *sound*. (Did you hear that *alliteration*?)

_____

Answers will vary.

_____

    Examples: The fools forgot that they found funny fudge.

_____

    The seven sisters will spur on the little son on to win the race.

_____

_____

Teacher Note: Read these words to your student *in the order found in the WG* and have him categorize them. You purposely want to read them in a scrambled order (not how they're listed above) so that he has to think about the first sound of each word and determine where to write it.

1. *Quotation marks* are used at the beginning and at the end of the exact words someone has said.

   "I like that!" shouted the boy.

2. A *comma* is used at the end of a *sentence tag* when we introduce a *quote*.

   The mother said, "It's time to eat!"

3. A *capital letter* is used at the beginning of every *quoted sentence.* The *end mark* of the last sentence of the *quote* is inside the *closing quotation marks*.

4. Write the sentences your teacher dictates to you, using the correct punctuation, including capital letters, periods, commas, question marks, and *quotation marks*.

Grandma had a role as good as gold. She cooked grain for supper, shined the spurs, fed the birds,

found the game I lost, and made a funny card saying, "How many gallons in an inch? How many

sisters in a pinch? How much wisdom in seven fools? Can you name eleven rules? I forgot but don't

be blue. Always know that I love you."

Teacher Notes:
1. Using all of this punctuation is still new for young students. Provide assistance as necessary for him. Here are some ways to do that.
   a. Before starting the first sentence, ask your student, "What tells my reader that I'm starting a sentence?" (a capital letter)
   b. At the end of that sentence, "How do I tell my reader I am done?" (a period at the end)
2. The words from List J-4 are underlined above.
3. Some of the words in this assignment will be taught later, but you can assist your student in writing them now.

cook (J-6)	made (J-5)	rule (N-1)
shine (O-2)	pinch (not in WG)	always (N-6)
fed (not in WG)	wisdom (S-6)	know (L-4)

1. Take a quiz on some of this week's spelling words. They are *adjectives* and *nouns*. Correct your quiz.

2. An *adjective* modifies (restricts or changes) the meaning of a noun or pronoun.

    sad son   *glad* son   *funny* son   *fine* son

3. Mix and match *adjectives* with the *nouns* and write Noun Phrases in the "Adjective + Noun" column below. Be sure to use each of your *adjectives* and *nouns*.

Adjectives			
seven	blue	gold	grand
funny	eleven	lost	hard

Nouns	Adjectives + Nouns = Noun Phrases
sisters	answers will vary Example: *funny sisters* or *eleven sisters*
card	
bird	
fools	
inch	
supper	
grain	
game	
spur	
role	

Teacher Notes:
1. Dictate the words in the "Adjectives" chart and in the "Nouns" column to your student.
2. Help as necessary as he combines his *adjectives* with *nouns* to form Adjective + Noun Phrases.

4. Write a complete sentence using one of your *adjective* and *noun* phrases.

_____

_____

_____

_____

1. Take a quiz on some review words and on some of this week's spelling words.

2. Correct your quiz so that everything is spelled correctly.

3. Mix and match your spelling words with one another or add review words to them to create a *compound word* for each new spelling word.

Review Words			
child	dog	mother	son
daddy	fish	red	step

Spelling Word	Compound Word
blue	bluebird, bluefish
gold	goldfish
grand	grandchild, grandson, granddaddy, grandmother
sisters	stepsisters
bird	redbird, bluebird, birddog

4. Write two complete sentences. Use one of your new *compound words* in each sentence.

_____

_____

_____

_____

_____

_____

1. Take a quiz on some review words and on some of your new spelling words.

2. Correct your quiz so that everything is spelled correctly.

3. How will you change these *verbs* into their *past tense form*? Only two of these *verbs* will use the ED past tense ending; the rest are *irregular*.

Present Tense Verbs	Past Tense Verbs
say	said
strike	struck
make	made
want	wanted
forgive	forgave
win	won
rest	rested

Teacher Note: The word *struck* won't come up until List O-2. However, you can introduce it now as the past tense of *strike*. Review rule #25 to help reinforce the CK at the end of the word.

4. Write a sentence using one of the *present tense verbs* and then write it again changing it into *past tense*. Do this one more time with another set of *present* and *past tense verbs*. When you're done you'll have four sentences.

Answers will vary.

Examples: I say "I love you" to my mother.

I said "I love you" to my mother.

He rests on his bed.

He rested on his bed.

Teacher Note: Notice that when using third person, the present tense verb needs an *-s* added to it. Watch for this in your student's writing.

Teacher Note: Teaching or reviewing the ED rule (#28) is recommended in the *preliminaries* for List J-5. **Suggestion:** Use this worksheet to help reinforce the rule before teaching the new spelling words, and then come back later in the week to practice writing with present and past tense verbs.

1. Listen carefully as your teacher dictates sentences with new and review spelling words. Write them on the lines below.

2. Correct your work so that everything is spelled correctly.

3. **Adverbs** are words that can be added to **verbs, adjectives,** or even other **adverbs** to answer these questions: *how?*   *where?*   *how much?*
   when?   *how long?*

4. **Adverbs** can be found in different places in a sentence.

5. In each of your sentences, hunt for the **adverb** that answers one or more of these questions and then (circle) it.

6. In the last column, write the question the **adverb** is answering.

Sentence	Question
What did he want the (most) ?	how much?
The room will be done (soon).	how long? OR when?
(Now) we won.	when?
(When) will you be kind?	when?
Are you (still) glad?	how long?
Will he (never) forgive?	how long?
Go (east) (then) turn at the rest stop.	where? & when?
I am (so) glad you like meat.	how much?
Do (not) strike your sister.	how?
(When) did he cover my toe?	when?

Teachers Notes:
1. There is enough room on the page for students to use more than one line if necessary. However, each new dictated sentence should start on a new line so that the adverb question lines up with it.
2. One adverb has two possible questions it answers.
3. One sentence includes two adverbs, each answering a different question.

1. A ***contraction*** is formed when we combine two words, remove one or more letters from one of the words, and replace the missing letter(s) with an ***apostrophe***.

    I + will = I'll   is + not = isn't   did + not = didn't

2. Three words that are commonly made into ***contractions*** include *not, is,* and *are*.

3. Write the word pairs your teacher dictates under the word that will be part of that ***contraction***.

4. Write the ***contraction*** with the ***apostrophe*** in the second column of each chart.

_____+ not	
can + not	can't
was + not	wasn't
has + not	hasn't
have + not	haven't

_____+ is	
he + is	he's
she + is	she's
it + is	it's
one + is	one's
here + is	here's
that + is	that's
what + is	what's

_____+ are	
you + are	you're

5. Write two sentences using a ***contraction*** in each sentence.

Teacher Notes:
1. The word pairs you will dictate are shown here in ***bold***.

2. Use this page if your student is using the Primary Learning Log.

3. Black Log users simply add these words to B21.

1. Take a quiz on some of your new spelling words.

2. Correct your quiz so that everything is spelled correctly.

3. Combine your spelling words with the *prefix* and/or the *suffixes* to create one *derivative* for each spelling word. Watch out for spelling rules you need to use to add endings to words!

Prefix
un-

Suffix	
-er	*-less*
-ern	*-ly*
-est	*-ness*
-ful	*-y*

Spelling Word	Derivative
said	unsaid
east	eastern
made	unmade
deep	deeper, deepest, deeply
still	stillness
glad	gladness, gladly, gladder, gladdest
forgive	forgiveness
rest	restless, restful
room	roomy
meat	meatless, meaty
air	airy
kind	unkind, kinder, kindest, kindly
joy	joyless, joyful

Teacher Notes:
1. To add *-er* or *-est* to the word *glad,* you'll need the 1-1-1 Rule (#14). See SWR pp 156- 158.

2. The suffix *-ful* is applying the Dismiss L Rule (#21). See SWR pp 176-177.

1. ***Quotation marks*** are used at the beginning and at the end of the exact words someone has said.

    "May I have one?" asked the girl.

2. A ***comma*** is used at the end of a ***sentence tag*** when we introduce a ***quote***.

    The daddy asked, "Is that yours?"

3. A ***capital letter*** is used at the beginning of every ***quoted sentence.*** The ***end mark*** of the last sentence of the ***quote*** is inside the ***closing quotation marks***.

4. Write about a discussion two people had about transportation.

5. Use the correct punctuation such as capital letters, periods, commas, and at least two quotes with ***quotation marks***.

Teacher Note:
1. See WG pg 48 for instructions and SWR Step #23 for instructions on teaching writing.

2. Have your student brainstorm what he will write on separate paper first. Planning what to write first makes writing so much easier.

3. Have him write a rough draft and edit it before rewriting it in his best penmanship on this page.

4. Putting ideas, words, correct spelling, proper grammar, *and* punctuation together is a *lot* to remember for a young student. When the student writes independently, much of the punctuation will be caught in the editing process.

1. Take a quiz in the first column below on some of your spelling words. Correct your work.

2. All of these words are *nouns*, which means they can be more than one or *plural*.

3. Write the *plural* form of each *noun* in the second column.

Single Noun	Plural Noun
town	towns
car	cars
train	trains
boat	boats
cook	cooks
egg	eggs
farm	farms
rock	rocks
fire	fires
chair	chairs

4. Write a sentence using one of these *plural nouns*.

Answers will vary.

Example: I will take three boats to get to the new farm.

1. Take a quiz on some of your spelling words. Correct your quiz so that everything is spelled correctly.

2. *Adjectives* describe *nouns.* Match your *nouns* with each of the *adjectives* that are on the same line and write them beneath the boxes below.

3. Illustrate the difference the change of *adjectives* makes to these *nouns.*

Nouns	Adjectives		
eggs	cooked	brown	large
fire	town	boat	cook

cooked eggs

Teacher Note:
Sample illustrations and available combinations are shown. The student can write his adjective/noun combinations on the page in any order he wants.

town fire

brown eggs

boat fire

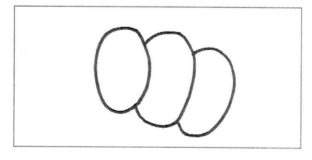

large eggs

cook fire

1. Take a quiz on some review words and on some of your new spelling words.

2. Correct your quiz so that everything is spelled correctly.

3. Combine your spelling words with the review words to create one *compound word* for each spelling word.

Review Words			
arm	down	life	ship
back	foot	never	side
box	hand	over	stone
day	house	plant	up

Spelling Word	Compound Word
more	moreover, nevermore
town	downtown, uptown, township, townhouse
car	boxcar
boat	houseboat, boathouse, lifeboat
cook	overcook, cookhouse
brown	brownstone
egg	eggplant
farm	farmhouse
work	footwork, housework, overwork, workhouse, workday
stay	overstay
sleep	oversleep, sleepover
fire	firearm, backfire, firehouse, fireside

Wise Guide
Enrichment Activity
Worksheets

Lists K-1 to K-7

1. Take a quiz on three of your new spelling words.

2. Correct your quiz so that everything is spelled correctly.

3. Combine your spelling words with the *suffixes* to create as many *derivatives* for each spelling word as you can.

Suffixes	
-er	*-ing*
-est	*-ly*

Spelling Word	Derivative
seem	seemly
	seeming
round	roundly
	rounder
	roundest
	rounding
clean	cleanly
	cleanest
	cleaner
	cleaning

Teacher Notes:

1. Simply dictate these three words in the first column.

2. If you haven't done so yet, make a copy of WG pg 98, cut apart the *suffix cards*, and save for *suffix* activities like this one. Create a flash card for the three words (or have the student do that for added practice). Demonstrate how to mix and match the *suffixes* with each word card to create legitimate English words.

3. The student records his findings in the second column.

1. Take a quiz on some of your new spelling words. Correct your work.

2. A *base word* is a word in its simplest form that has nothing added to it. We add *prefixes* or *suffixes* to *base words* to make *derivatives*. When we combine *base words* to create *compound words*, we're making yet another kind of *derivative*.

3. This week's words are a puzzle of *base words* and *derivatives*. You've written the *base words*, now find the *derivatives* in your List K-1 spelling words and write them in the second column.

Base Word	Derivative
two	twin
	between
	twenty
	twice
	twelve
	twelfth
see	seen
	seem
may	maybe
with	without
male	female
round	around
sum	summary
night	tonight
clean	cleanse
some	someone

Teacher Note: Have the student write his words only in the open spaces in this first column.

1. An **antonym** is a word that means the opposite of something else. For example, *up & down* or *big & little* are **antonyms**.

2. Read the words in the first column. Which of your spelling words are the **antonyms**? Write them in the second column.

3. Are there some left that you're not sure about? Listen as your teacher reads your spelling words to you. Write the last ones.

Antonym	Spelling Word
male	female
dirty	clean
today	tonight
within	without
no one	someone
flat	round

1. Your teacher will dictate two sentences to you. Write them neatly and correctly on the lines below.

2. To use correct punctuation, ask yourself these questions.

   a. What goes at the beginning of a sentence to tell the reader you're starting an idea?

   b. What goes at the end of a sentence to tell the reader you are done with that idea?

   c. Is there any time that your teacher's voice pauses, letting you know where to put a *comma*?

___

Maybe tonight someone between twelve and twenty can clean twice around the room.

___

In summary, have the two of you seen a male with a female twin?

___

Teacher Notes:
1. Before starting each sentence, ask the student question a.

2. At the end of each sentence, ask the student question b.

3. Before dictating the second sentence, ask question c. and then exaggerate the pause at the comma.

1. Take a quiz on your new spelling words. Correct your quiz so that everything is spelled correctly.

2. *Adjectives* describe *nouns*, adding more vivid details and answering questions that clarify the *noun*.

3. Listen as your teacher reads some sentences that include the *nouns* you wrote.

4. Say aloud the *adjective* that *describes* each *noun*.

5. Which question is that *adjective* answering? Put a check mark in the appropriate column for that question. Sometimes an *adjective* can answer more than one question, so choose which question you think is best.

Spelling Word	What kind?	Which one?	How many?	Whose?
story	✓	✓		
shore	✓	✓		
oak	✓	✓		
hour	✓	✓		
cent			✓	
wheat	✓			
bone	✓	✓		
camp	✓	✓		
fly	✓	✓		
lady	✓	✓		
drive		✓		
wood	✓	✓		
drink	✓	✓		
start	✓			
head	✓			
fruit	✓			
pole	✓	✓		
plane	✓	✓		
tone	✓			

Teacher Notes:
1. Dictate the words in the first column.
2. Read the sentences from WG pg 56, having your student determine which word is describing the *noun* he wrote and which question it is answering.
3. Note that the sentence for the word *better* in the WG has been omitted. Do not dictate this sentence for the *adjective* part of the assignment.
4. Multiple possibilities are listed for some words, but *only one check per word* is necessary.

1. **Adjectives** describe **nouns,** adding more vivid details and answering questions that clarify the **noun**. Some of your List K spelling words can be **nouns** and **adjectives**.

2. Write _____ sentences below using your spelling words. Use **adjectives** to describe the **nouns** in your sentences.

3. Draw an arrow from the **adjective** to the **noun** it is describing.

   I like to hear the story lady read the better book.

4. Use proper punctuation in your sentences.

Teacher Notes:
1. Select the number of sentences you want your student to write and add that to the instructions for #2.

2. Have him hunt for words that could be used as *nouns* and *adjectives* in his List K-1 and K-2 spelling words. Keep in mind that words can change their part of speech depending on how they are used.

1. Take a quiz on some review words, some of your new spelling words, and four bonus words.

2. Correct your quiz so that everything is spelled correctly.

3. Combine your words to create one *compound word* for each spelling word.

Review Words				Bonus Words
air	fire	red	under	cake
back	like	sea	up	flag
book	line	ship	way	grape
bug	over	teller	work	horse

Spelling Word	Compound Word
story	storybook, storyteller,
shore	shoreline
wheat	**wheatcake**
bone	backbone
camp	campfire
fly	firefly, **horsefly**
lady	ladybug, ladylike
drive	overdrive, driveway
wood	redwood, backwoods, woodwork
start	upstart
head	headship, headline, overhead, redhead, airhead
fruit	**fruitcake, grapefruit**
pole	**flagpole**
plane	airplane
tone	overtone, undertone

Teacher Notes:
1. The *bonus words* have not yet been taught, but you can easily teach them now for this activity. Compound words made from these bonus words are listed in *bold*.

2. If you're not including these bonus words, don't dictate the spelling words *wheat, fruit,* or *pole*, thus leaving three empty lines at the bottom of the page.

1. Take a quiz on some of your new spelling words in the first column.

2. Correct your quiz so that everything is spelled correctly.

3. Combine your spelling words with the *suffixes* to create two *derivatives* for each spelling word. Watch out for some E's Dropping words!

Suffixes	
-ed	-less
-er	-ly
-ing	

Teacher Note: Have your student use the *suffix cards* from WG pg 98 to mix and match with a flash card for each word to discover legitimate English words. The student records his findings in the last two columns.

Spelling Word	Derivative	Derivative
finish	finished, finisher,	finishing
clear	cleared, clearing,	clearly
reach	reached	reaching
delay	delayed, delayer,	delaying
hurt	hurter, hurting,	hurtless
move	moved, mover, moving,	movingly
test	tested, tester,	testing
care	cared, caring, careless,	carelessly
spell	spelled,* speller,	spelling
state	stated, stating,	stately
price	priced, pricing,	priceless
base	based, basing,	baseless
bake	baked, baker,	baking
burn	burned, burner,	burning
fail	failed, failing,	failingly

Teacher Note: *See WG pg 58 for more on British spellings.

1. Take a quiz on some review words and on some verbs from List K-3. Correct your quiz so that everything is spelled correctly.

2. *Helping verbs* are little words that we use in front of *verbs* to give them more exact meaning or to change the tense.

3. Mix and match the *helping verbs* with the *verbs* to create *verb phrases*.

Helping Verbs	
shall	would
should	could

Verbs	Verb Phrase
finish	Answers will vary.
clear	Examples: shall finish, would reach
reach	
delay	
hurt	
move	
test	
care	
spell	
state	
price	
base	
bake	
burn	
fail	

                                                                   WG pg 59

1. Take a quiz on some of your new spelling words in the first column. Watch for E's Dropping words!
2. Correct your quiz so that everything is spelled correctly.
3. Combine your spelling words with the *prefixes* to create one *derivative* for each open space.

Spelling Word	mis-	un-
finished		unfinished
clear		unclear
reached		unreached
sent		unsent
delayed		undelayed
hurt		unhurt
moved		unmoved
tested		untested
caring		uncaring
spelled	misspelled	
stated	misstated	unstated
priced		unpriced
based		unbased
baked		unbaked
burned		unburned
failing		unfailing

Teacher Notes: Notice that the prefix *mis-* added to a base word that starts with an S creates a double consonant between the syllables.

4. Write a sentence using one of your new derivatives.

_____

_____

_____

1. We form *contractions* when we combine two words, remove one or more letters from one of the words, and replace the missing letter(s) with an *apostrophe*.

    I + will = I'll   is + not = isn't   did + not = didn't

2. Three of this week's words are commonly made into *contractions*. Write them from your teacher's dictation in the first column.

3. Combine these *helping verbs* with *not* to form *contractions* in the second column.

4. Write the pronouns your teacher dictates in the third column and a *helping verb* in the title line.

5. Combine each pronoun with the *helping verb* to form more *contractions* in the last column.

_____ + not	
would	wouldn't
should	shouldn't
could	couldn't

_____ + ___would___	
I	I'd
you	you'd
he	he'd
she	she'd
we	we'd
they	they'd (advanced option)

Teacher Notes:
(1) Dictate the words in the first and third columns (shown in *bold*), and (2) the word *would* in the title line of the second chart.

The word *they* will be taught in List K-7, but you can teach it now if you like.

5. Write two sentences using one of these *contractions* in each sentence.

Answers will vary.

Example: I wouldn't reach for that if I were you.

He'd take that test so he cold play baseball sooner.

Teacher Note:
1. Use this page if your student is using the Primary Learning Log.
2. Black Log users simply add these words to B21.

1. Take a quiz on some of your new spelling words.

2. Correct your quiz so that everything is spelled correctly.

3. Combine your spelling words with each of the *suffixes* to create *two derivatives* for each spelling word. What rule do you need to use with words that end with a Silent Final E?

Spelling Word	*-ly*	*-ness*
open	openly	openness
bare	barely	bareness
high	highly	highness
weak	weakly	weakness
grave	gravely	graveness
light	lightly	lightness
easy	**easily**	**easiness** ←

Teacher Note:
Dictate *easy* only if your student has learned the Y's Exchanging Rule (#24) since its derivatives *easily* and *easiness* need this rule. If your student hasn't learned that yet, use the review word *dark* and its derivatives *darkly* and *darkness*.

4. Write two sentences using *derivatives* you created. Use an *-ly* word in one sentence and a *-ness* word in the other sentence.

Answers will vary.

Examples: I found the weakness in her game.

The fire barely burned as there was little wood.

1. Take a quiz on a few of your new spelling words.

2. Correct your quiz so that everything is spelled correctly.

3. You can add the *prefix un-* to two of these spelling words. Which ones are they?

4. Write the new *derivatives* in the second column.

Spelling Word	un-
these	
opened	unopened
city	
shut	
easy	uneasy

5. Write a sentence for each of your new *derivatives*.

Answers will vary.

Examples: The window was unopened.

Daddy was uneasy about the game the baby was playing.

1. Take a quiz on some review words and on some of your new spelling words.

2. Correct your quiz so that everything is spelled correctly.

3. Combine your spelling words with one another and with the review words to create one *compound word* for each spelling word.

Review Words			
eat	house	moon	place
foot	in	one	way
head	land	over	yard

Spelling Word	Compound Word
any	anyplace, anyway, anyone
bare	barefoot
high	highlight, highland, highway
coming	incoming, overcoming
ant	anteater
first	firsthand, headfirst
grave	graveyard
light	houselight, headlight, highlight, moonlight

4. Write two sentences using one of your new *compound words* in each sentence.

Answers will vary.

Examples:

Anyplace you want to go will work for me.

The incoming plane has no headlights.

1.   Choose six of this week's spelling words to illustrate, one in each box below.

2.   Write the word on the line beneath its picture.

Teacher Note: Sample illustrations can be found on WG pg 61. The student may choose different words or to illustrate these words differently.

1. Take a quiz on some review words, some of your new spelling words, and a new word.

2. Correct your quiz so that everything is spelled correctly.

3. Combine your spelling words with the review words to create one *compound word* for each spelling word. Two words will also need a *suffix* to make a real English word.

Review Words		
ball	house	man
bow	less	over
box	let	ship
do	like	some
fall	load*	

Spelling Word	Compound Word
bear	overbearing
rain	rainbow, rainfall
fear	fearsome, fearless
evil	evildoer
mail	mailbox, mailman
night	nightfall, overnight
king	kingship, kinglike
queen	queenlike
party	houseparty
basket	basketball
cloud	cloudless
eye	eyeball, eyelet
wagon	wagonload

Teacher Notes:
1. Teach the new word *load** now.
2. Add the *suffix -ing* to make this compound word.
3. Add the *suffix -er* to make this compound word.

1. Take a quiz on some of some of your recent spelling words.

2. Correct your quiz so that everything is spelled correctly.

3. Combine your spelling words with the *suffix -ly* to create a *derivative* for each spelling word.

Spelling Word	Derivative
seem	seemly
round	roundly
clean	cleanly
hour	hourly
clear	clearly
state	stately
base	basely
open	openly
high	highly
first	firstly
weak	weakly
grave	gravely
light	lightly
single	singly
earth	earthly
evil	evilly
night	nightly
king	kingly
queen	queenly
easy	**easily** ←
thirsty	**thirstily** ←

Teacher Notes:
1. Dictate *easy* and *thirsty* only if your student has learned the Y's Exchanging Rule (#24) since its derivatives *easily* and *thirstily* need this rule.

2. If your student hasn't learned that yet, use the following review words from List J.
   near - nearly
   kind - kindly

1. Good writers play with language to make it more interesting and fun for the reader.

2. One technique you can add to your writing is called **alliteration,** which is where a **sound** is repeated at the beginning of several words of a sentence. Read this sentence and listen for the **sound** that is repeated.   *The cat called for her kittens when they cried for milk.*

3. Read your List K spelling words out loud and listen carefully for words that start with the /k/ **sound**. Write them in that column below. Repeat for the /g/, /h/, /s/, and /w/ **sounds**.

4. Reminders:
   a. The letter inside the slashes indicates a **sound**, not necessarily how the word is spelled.

   b. You must listen for the **sound** at the beginning of a word. For example, words that start with the single-letter phonogram C could be added to either the /k/ or the /s/ list, depending on what the phonogram is saying in that word. Other letters can also say the /k/ sound, so listen for them in some of your words.

/k/	/g/	/h/	/s/	/w/
clean	grave	head	seem	without
cleanse	garden	hurt	seen	wood
camp	gift	high	summary	would
could	goose	horse	someone	weak
clear	glass	hero	story	window
care			cent	wagon
coming			start	wife
cotton			sent	week
king			spell	
queen			state	
cloud			city	
crime			single	
class			stick	
club			stamp	
			set	

Teacher Notes: Many times the phonogram K is our first choice at the beginning of a word when we cannot use C because of an E, I, or Y coming after it (rule #2).

The QU phonogram is made with the sounds /kw/.

Teacher Notes: *Hour* doesn't go in this list since the H is silent; the first sound is /ow/.

The SH phonogram doesn't make the /s/ sound, so we won't use words like **shore** or **shall**.

Teacher Note: The phonogram WH says a different sound than W, so the words **wheat** and **where** won't go in the /w/ list.

1. Look at your *Alliterations* worksheet.

2. Use <u>at least three</u> of the words from the /k/ list to write a sentence. You're free to add more words to really saturate the sentence with your *sounds*. (Did you hear that *alliteration*?)

3. Repeat this process with each of the other lists from the worksheet. You'll have five *alliteration* sentences when you're done.

Answers will vary.

Examples: The queen with her clean cotton robe, could not clearly see the crime.

Without wood, a window would be too weak to withstand a wagon crash.

The hero hurt the head of his horse.

The garden was a grave site for the glass goose.

Someone needs to start a story about a state spelling game.

1. Take a quiz on some review words, some of your new spelling words, and one new word.

2. Correct your quiz so that everything is spelled correctly.

3. Combine your spelling words with the review words to create one *compound word* for each spelling word.

Review Words		
back	fly	saw
drum*	hour	shot
day	house	some
end	out	step
eye	room	yard

Teacher Note: Teach the new word *drum** now.

Spelling Word	Compound Word
stick	drumstick, yardstick
horse	horsefly, sawhorse, horseback
week	weekday, weekend
brother	stepbrother
glass	eyeglass, hourglass
class	classroom, outclass
wife	housewife
ear	eardrum, earshot

4. Write a sentence using one of your new words.

Answers will vary. Examples:

Could you help me get the horsefly to go out of the house?

Her stepbrother is a happy boy.

1. *Abbreviations* use a few letters to represent a larger word. You've learned several *abbreviations* by now.

2. As your teacher dictates some review words to you, write them in the "Spelling Word" columns below. Correct your work.

3. Now add the *abbreviations* for each of these words.

4. Write two sentences that include some *abbreviations*.

Abbreviation	Spelling Word		Abbreviation	Spelling Word	
@	at	C	E	east	J-5
St.	Street	D	lg.	large	J-6
yr.	year	H-1	12th	twelfth	K-1
yd.	yard	H-2	w/o	without	K-1
ft.	foot, feet	I-2 & I-3	hr.	hour	K-2
ea.	each	I-2	Dr.	Drive, Doctor	K-2
Mr.	Mister	I-3	1st	first	K-4
W	west	I-3	lgt.	light	K-4
w/	with	J-1	lb.	pound	K-6
gal.	gallon	J-4	bro.	brother	K-6
in.	inch	J-4	wk.	week	K-6

Answers will vary.

Examples: Dr. Graves lives at 312 Wood Dr.

I will find two ears of corn for 50 cents ea. on the 1st of May.

Teacher Notes:
1. The Wise Lists where these abbreviations were taught are listed above in **bold** for the *teacher's reference* only. The student does not need to make note of them.

2. Use this page if your student is using the Primary Learning Log.

3. Black Log users simply add these words to B25.

1. As your teacher dictates your spelling words, write them in their *plural* form in the part of the *Plurals Rule* they are following.

2. Correct your work to be sure everything is spelled correctly.

To make a word plural, just add an -S:	
freedoms	clubs
pounds	ears
sticks	weeks
gifts	titles
afternoons	stamps
horses*	sets
brothers	
UNLESS the word ending hisses:	
classes	glasses
horses*	
Changes:	
wives	knives
loaves	
Ends with O:	
heroes	
Internal change:	
geese	

Teacher Note:
*See WG pg 65 for an explanation as to why *horses* could be added to either the *"Just add -s"* OR the *"ending hisses"* categories. Let your student choose.

1. Take a quiz on some of your spelling words. There are four new words. Correct your work.

2. The word *homophones* comes from the Greek language. *homos* = "same"   *phon* = "sound"

3. *Homophones* are words that sound alike but have different spellings and meanings.

   sea - see   *son - sun*   *won - one*

4. Do you know the other words that complete the *homophone* pairs for the words you wrote? Read through your spelling words from List K-1 to K-7 to find them. Write the words you find next to their partners below.

Homophone Pairs			
to	C	two	K-1
seam	*	seem	K-2
our	J-1	hour	K-2
cent	K-2	sent	K-3
wood	K-2	would	K-3
hi	*	high	K-4

Homophone Pairs			
bare	K-4	bear	K-5
male	K-1	mail	K-5
knight	*	night	K-5
I	C	eye	K-5
weak	K-4	week	K-6
oh	*	owe	K-7

5. Write two sentences in which each sentence contains a *homophone* pair.

Answers will vary.

   Examples: It would seem I have a rip in my seam.

   He would like to cut some wood.

Teacher Notes:
1. Use this page if your student is using the Primary Learning Log.
2. Black Log users simply add these words to B38.

Teacher Notes (con't):
3. The words you are to dictate are in **bold** above.
4. The lists where these spelling words can be found are listed above *for the teacher's reference only*.
5. The following words* are are not included in the Wise Guide, but they can easily be taught now for this activity.
   seam
   hi - informal for *hello,* an interjection
   oh - an interjection for surprise
   knight

1. Choose three pairs of *homophones* that you have learned so far and illustrate them in the boxes below.

2. Label your *homophones*.

> **Teacher Note:** Sample illustrations are shown below. The student may choose different words or to illustrate these words differently.

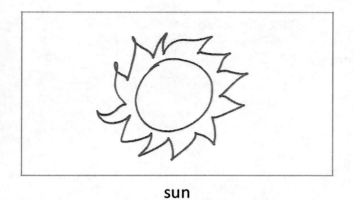

sun

son

bear

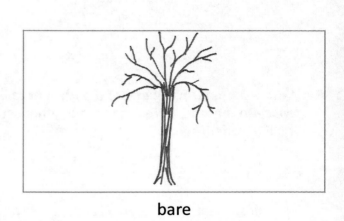

bare

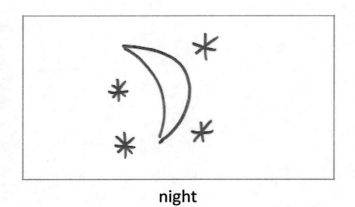

night

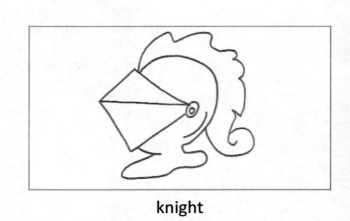

knight

1. Take a quiz on some review words and some of your new spelling words.

2. Correct your quiz so that everything is spelled correctly.

3. How will you change these **verbs** into their **past tense form**? Only two of these **verbs** will use the ED past tense ending; the rest are **irregular**.

Present Tense Verbs	Past Tense Verbs
draw	drew
feel	felt
owe	owed
keep	kept
join	joined
grow	grew
cost	cost

> **Teacher Note:** Two of the words won't be taught until later (*drew* - L-4 & *feel* - N-5) and two words are not included in the Wise List (*kept, grew*). You can introduce them now.

4. Write a sentence using one of the **present tense verbs** and then write it again changing it into **past tense**. Do this one more time with another set of **present** and **past tense verbs**. When you're done you'll have four sentences.

Answers will vary.

Examples: I feel sad when my cat is not playing with me.

I felt sad when my cat was not playing with me.

You grow up nice and big.

You grew up nice and big.

1. Take a quiz on some single-letter phonograms in the "Letter" columns below.

2. Listen as your teacher reads your spelling words to you. Write the word next to the letter that is at the beginning of each of your spelling words.

3. When you're done with your quiz, your words will now be in *alphabetical* order!

4. Correct any errors.

Letter	Spelling Word	Letter	Spelling Word
a	across	l	lion
b	behind	m	mile
c	cost	o	owe
d	draw	p	poor
e	even	r	rung
f	felt	s	sir
g	grow	t	they
h	herd	u	upon
j	join	w	water
k	keep	z	zero

Teacher Note:
Only 20 of the 26 letters of the alphabet are included on this page. Dictate only what's on the page or you'll run out of room.

Teacher Notes:
1. Dictate the single-letter phonograms to your student, using phonogram sounds.
2. Read the List K-7 words to your student *in the order listed in the WG*. You purposely want to read them in a scrambled order (not how they're listed on this worksheet) so that he has to think about how to match the word with the letter that is at the beginning.

3. **Alternative way to teach alphabetizing.**
   a. Dictate the spelling words to the student for a quiz, having him write each word on a 3x5 card.
   b. Correct any errors. Spread the cards out on the table upside down.
   c. Show him the alphabet on a chart or on a letter strip. Practice identifying the next three letters at any given starting point. (For example, say "L, M, N…" and he needs to finish with "O, P, Q.")
   d. Select two cards and demonstrate how to put them on the table in alphabetical order, from left to right.
   e. Select another card and add it to the first two alphabetized cards in the correct placement. Continue until you have all 20 cards in alphabetical order, from left to right.
   f. Gather the cards, keeping them in alphabetical order.
   g. Proceed with the assignment as explained above in #1 & #2.
   h. Have the student read each card from his stack of cards and compare them with the words he wrote on the worksheet. They should match. He can now alphabetize words based on their first letter!

1. We form **contractions** when we combine two words, remove one or more letters from one of the words, and replace the missing letter(s) with an **apostrophe**.

    I + will = I'll   *is + not = isn't*   *did + not = didn't*

2. Write the word pairs from your teacher's dictation in the first column.

3. Combine these **pronouns** and **helping or state of being verbs** to form **contractions** in the second column.

Contractions	
they + are	they're
we + are	we're
they + have	they've
we + have	we've
they + will	they'll
we + will	we'll
they + would	they'd
we + would	we'd

Teacher Note: Dictate the words in the first column (shown in **bold**). The student will complete the second column on his own.

5. Write two sentences using one of these **contractions** and a different **pronoun** in each sentence.

Answers will vary.

Example: They're here for you now.

We'd like to go with you to the zoo.

Teacher Note:
1. Use this page if your student is using the Primary Learning Log.
2. Black Log users simply add these words to B21.

1. Take a quiz on 29 of your review words. Correct your work.

2. All of these words can be used as *prepositions*, which are words that show a *relationship* between a *noun* and another word in the sentence.

> The child is *in* the tub.   The *preposition* tells us how the *child* is related to the *tub* (in).

3. The *preposition* and the *noun* following it are called a *prepositional phrase* (*in the tub*).

Prepositions					
in	C	of	C	from	J-2
by	C	like	E	along	J-5
out	C	for	G	near	J-6
to	C	about	H-1	between	K-1
into	C	after	I-1	without	K-1
up	C	down	I-4	around	K-1
on	C	with	J-1	upon	K-7
onto	extra	under	J-1	across	K-7
over	C	outside	J-2	behind	K-7
at	C	inside	J-2		

4. Write two sentences, using your K-7 spelling words and a *prepositional phrase* in each one. Underline your *prepositional phrases*.

Answers will vary.

   Examples: The lion ran <u>after the herd</u> <u>of elephants</u>.

   They will join us <u>in the water</u>.

Teacher Notes:
1. For more on teaching *prepositional phrases*, refer to the Answer Key for "Helping Verbs Sentences" on page 72.

Teacher Notes (con't):
2. The places where these prepositions were first introduced in the WG are listed above *for the teacher's reference only*.

3. Use this page if your student is using the Primary Learning Log.

4. Black Log users add any of these words to B30 if not already done so.

Wise Guide
Enrichment Activity
Worksheets

Lists L-1 to L-6

1. Take a quiz on some review words, your new spelling words, and one new word.

2. Correct your quiz so that everything is spelled correctly.

3. Combine your spelling words with the review words to create one **compound word** for each spelling word.

Review Words			
back	law	out	time
ball	light	over	top
bed	like	side	turn
bird	line	slap	under
box	mail	sleep	way
in	man	stand	yard

Teacher Note: The word *slap* is not taught in the WG, but you can easily include it here for this activity.

Spelling Word	Compound Word
talk	backtalk, outtalk
walk	walkin, walkout, sidewalk, walkway, sleepwalk, Walkman
country	countryman, countryside
half	halfway, halftime
done	overdone, underdone
gone	undergone
soap	soapbox, soaplike
black	blackout, blacktop, blackball, blackbird, blackmail, blacklight
clothes	bedclothes, clothesline, underclothes
clothing	underclothing

Spelling Word	Compound Word
power	overpower
road	roadbed, inroad, roadside, roadway
stream	streamline, streamlike
church	churchyard, churchlike
dash	slapdash
feed	overfeed, underfeed
news	newsstand, newsman
suit	lawsuit, undersuit, suitlike
table	turntable, timetable
dead	deadline, deadlight

1. Take a quiz on three review spelling words on the first line of each of the columns below. Correct your quiz so that everything is spelled correctly.

2. Silent Final E words commonly lose the need for the E when adding a *vowel suffix*.

3. Combine your spelling words with these *suffixes* to create as many *derivatives* for each spelling word as you can. Watch for that E's Dropping Rule!

Suffixes				
-ed	-er	-est	-ing	-ly

owe	bare	fine
owed	bared	fined
owing	barest	finer
	baring	finest
	barely	fining
		finely

Teacher Notes:
1. Simply dictate the first word at the top of each column, listed above for you in *bold*.

2. If you haven't done so yet, make a copy of WG pg 98, cut apart the *suffix cards*, and save for *suffix* activities like this one. Create a flash card for the three words (or have the student do that for added practice), and then demonstrate how to mix and match the *suffixes* with each word card to create legitimate English words. The student records his findings below each *base word*.

1. In the first column, take a quiz on some of your spelling words. Correct your work.

2. The words you wrote are **action verbs**, meaning that they describe actions or what someone does.

3. **Verbs** also tell us **when** something happens, happened, or will happen. This is called **tense.** The **verbs** you wrote are in **present tense**, meaning it is something that happens regularly.

    I *sleep* at night.   I *eat* my dinner.   I *play* outside.

4. Practice adding the **ED ending** to your verbs to make them **past tense**. Write the new word in the correct column, depending on the sound the ED phonogram is saying. There is one **verb** that doesn't use the ED ending because it is **irregular.** Can you find it?

Present Tense	**ed**	2 **ed**	3 **ed**	**X**
talk			talked	
walk			walked	
soap			soaped	
clothe		clothed		
power		powered		
stream		streamed		
dash			dashed	
church			churched	
feed				fed
suit	suited			
table		tabled		
half		halved		

5. Write a sentence using one of these **past tense** verbs.

Answers will vary.

    Example: Dad powered up the truck to go to work.

        God clothed the birds air.

Teacher Notes:
1. Use this page if your student is using the Primary Learning Log.
2. Black Log users simply add these words to B19 & B20.

1. Take a quiz on some review words, some of your new spelling words, and a new word.

2. Correct your quiz so that everything is spelled correctly.

3. Combine your spelling words with the review words to create one ***compound word*** for each spelling word. On one word you'll have to add the ***suffix -ed*** to make a real English word.

Review Words			
back	here	light	side
hand	high	man	up
hay*	house	moon	word
	lace	over	

Spelling Word	Compound Word
ride	hayride, override
within	herewithin
stop	backstop, stoplight
pick	handpick, pickup
mind	highminded**
track	backtrack, sidetrack
mad	madman, madhouse
neck	necklace
honey	honeymoon
catch	catchword

Teacher Note:
*new word
**suffix *-ed*
    added

4. Write a sentence using one of your new ***compound words***.

Answers will vary.

Example: Let's go for a hayride!

Mother loved the necklace I gave her.

1. An *analogy* is a comparison between two things.

2. Look at the first pair of words and figure out the relationship between them. Then look at the second set of words. They share the same relationship as the first two.

>   Father is to Mother as boy is to _____girl_____.

>   In this example, the comparison (or the relationship) is gender opposites.

3. Below are pairs of words. The first pair relate to one another in some way. How are these words related? Use that same relationship to complete the second pair.

4. Use your spelling words from this week's list to complete each set of *analogies*.

Under is to over as below is to _____above_____.

Smile is to frown as happy is to ____mad_____.

Ship is to water as train is to _____track_____.

Door is to wall as gate is to _____fence_____.

Sour is to sweet as vinegar is to _____honey_____.

Give is to get as sell is to _____buy_____.

Feet are to walk as car is to _____ride_____.

Hand is to wrist as head is to _____neck_____.

All is to one as every is to _____once_____.

Give is to get as throw is to _____catch_____.

Weeds is to pull as flowers are to _____pick_____.

Drag is to shove as pull is to _____push_____.

1. Take a quiz on your spelling words in the first column. Correct your work.

2. Add the *suffix -ing* to each of your words in the second column to create a *derivative*. Which words need your *1-1-1 rule* to form a *derivative*?

3. In the last column write *1-1-1* when you have used the rule. If you weren't able to use the rule, explain why not with one of these reasons.

> — not a single vowel
> — not a single consonant

Spelling Word	Derivative	Rule? Why Not?
dash	dashing	not a single consonant
set	setting	1-1-1
stream	stream	not a single vowel
hop	hopping	1-1-1
soap	soaping	not a single vowel
shut	shutting	1-1-1
feed	feeding	not a single vowel
club	clubbing	1-1-1
walk	walking	not a single consonant
war	warring	1-1-1

Teacher Note: Adapt this assignment to a young student. Have him only write "1-1-1" when he uses the rule and *answer verbally* as to why he could not use it in the other situations.

4. Write a sentence using one of your new *1-1-1 derivatives*.

Answers will vary.

Examples: I am shutting the door for you.

I don't like the warring between brothers.

1. Take a quiz on some review words, some of your new spelling words, and a new word.

2. Correct your quiz so that everything is spelled correctly.

3. Combine your spelling words with the review words to create one *compound word* for each spelling word. On some words you'll have to add *suffixes* to make real English words.

Review Words			
book	house	pin*	sun
bone	lace	out	time
dog	land	over	up
head	life	ship	word
	pick	stand	

Teacher Note:
*new word
**added a suffix to create
 a real English word

Spelling Word	Compound Word
save	lifesaver
date	*outdated, update
rise	sunrise
war	wartime, warhead
own	**landowner
warm	**housewarming
turn	turnout, turnover, upturn
point	pinpoint, standpoint

Spelling Word	Compound Word
watch	watchdog, watchword, overwatch
wish	wishbone
battle	battleship
root	uproot
meet	**meetinghouse
pocket	pocketbook, pickpocket
shoe	horseshoe, shoelace

1.   Choose six of this week's spelling words to illustrate, one in each box below.

2.   Write the word on the line beneath its picture.

Teacher Note: Sample illustrations are shown below. The student may choose different words or to illustrate these words differently.

date

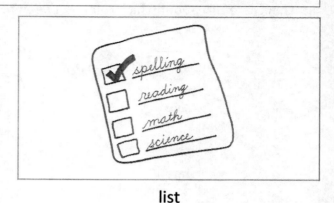

list

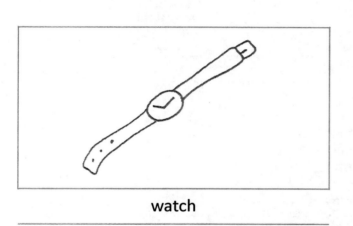

watch

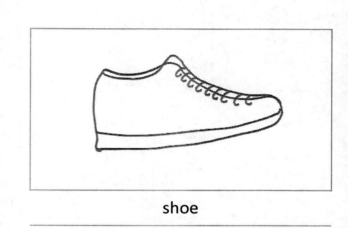

shoe

warm

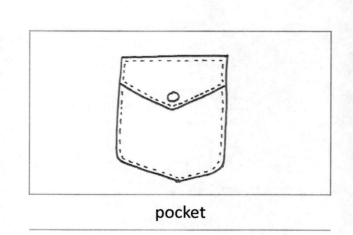

pocket

1. Take a quiz on your new spelling words in the first column. Correct your quiz.
2. A *base word* is a word in its simplest form that has nothing added to it. Sometimes, we add word parts called *prefixes* or *suffixes* to make *derivatives*.
3. Add the *suffix -ing* to each of your words to create *derivatives*.
4. Think carefully about which rules you need to use to add this word ending.

Spelling Word	-ing
save	saving
list	listing
date	dating
grant	granting
fight	fighting
rise	rising
hop	hopping
war	warring
own	owning
warm	warming
turn	turning
point	pointing
watch	watching
wish	wishing
battle	battling
march	marching
root	rooting
meet	meeting
shoe	shoeing
pocket	pocketing

Teacher Note: To retain the meaning of the base word, we keep the silent E in *shoeing*.

1. Take a quiz on your new spelling words in the first column. Correct your quiz.

2. A *base word* is a word in its simplest form that has nothing added to it. Sometimes, we add word parts called *prefixes* or *suffixes* to make *derivatives*.

3. Add the *suffix -ed* to each of your words to create *derivatives* in the second column. All but two of the words could also be used as a *noun*; write them in their *plural* forms in the last column.

4. Think carefully about which rules you need to use to add these endings.

Spelling Word	-ed	Plural (nouns only)
save	saved	saves
list	listed	lists
date	dated	dates
grant	granted	grants
fight	**fought**	fights
rise	**rose**	rises
hop	hopped	hops
war	warred	wars
own	owned	
warm	warmed	
turn	turned	turns
point	pointed	points
watch	watched	watches
wish	wished	wishes
battle	battled	battles
march	marched	marches
root	rooted	roots
meet	**met**	meets
shoe	**shod**	shoes
pocket	pocketed	pockets

Teacher Notes:

1. The student needs to have learned the ED & Plurals Rules to complete this page.

2. The words in **bold** are irregular past tense verbs. A young student probably won't know these new words and will need your help.

1. A *sentence* is a group of words that gives a sense of completeness. Every sentence needs a *subject* and a *verb*. The *subject* tells what the sentence is about, and the *verb* tells us something about it.

    A dog was barking.   Who/what is this sentence about?   dog - *subject*
                            What about the [*subject*]?   was barking - *verb*

2. As your teacher reads your spelling words in some sentences, write the simple *subject* and the *verb* of each sentence in the correct columns below. New words are listed in the box below.

	Subject	Verb
1	mother	held
2	men	know
3	nothing	can cut
4	we	were **praising**
5	body	is
6	she	rode
7	butcher	knows
8	He	rose
9	kitchen	**needs**
10	edge	is made
11	we	close
12	climate	makes
13	birds	flew
14	ground	drank
15	**spirits**	fell
16	trip	ended
17	**artist**	drew
18	flower	is
19	flour	**spilled**
20	stair	**slants**

Teacher Notes:
1. Read the words and their sentences *in the order they occur on WG* pg 76.

2. Words in **bold** on this answer key will either be taught later or are not in the Wise List. You can easily teach them now.

praising (M-3)
needs (N-3)
spirits (N-3)
artist (not in WG)
spilled (not in WG)
slants (not in WG)

1. Take a quiz on some review words, some of your new spelling words, and a new word.

2. Correct your quiz so that everything is spelled correctly.

3. Combine your spelling words with the review words to create one *compound word* for each spelling word. Sometimes you might need to add the *suffix -s* to make a real word.

Review Words			
any	back	bush*	down
every	may	no	over
play	some	sun	up
way	under	with	work

Spelling Word	Compound Word
body	anybody, everybody, somebody, nobody
ground	playground, background, underground, groundwork
stair	stairway, downstairs**, upstairs**
flower	Mayflower, sunflower
rose	rosebush
drew	withdrew, overdrew
held	withheld, upheld

Teacher Notes:
**bush* = new word

****Add the *suffix -s*
make real English
words.

4. Write a sentence using one of your new *compound words.*

Answers will vary.

Examples: The dog fell down the stairway.

Dad withheld our snack until our work was done.

1. In this List L-4 we see four kinds of word variations.

    a. **Homograph:** Words that sound and look alike, but they mean something very different.
        bat (animal), *bat* (used in baseball)

    b. **Heteronyms:** Words that look exactly alike, but they do not sound alike.
        do (act), *do* (first note on musical scale)

    c. **Homophones:** Words that sound exactly alike, but they do not look alike.
        meet (get together), *meat* (food)

    d. **Commonly Confused:** Words with different meanings but are often confused because they sound similar.   *finally* (at last), *finely* (done in a fine manner)

2. The first word of each pair is written for you. Write the spelling word that finishes the pair.

3. Draw pictures to show what each word means.

TEACHER NOTE: Definitions are provided for each word. When word pairs are spelled the same, the student's pictures may be reversed from this answer key.

Homographs		Homographs	
a flower	past tense of *to rise*	the solid surface of the earth	past tense of *to grind*
rose	rose	ground	ground

Homographs		Homographs	
to fall over something	a vacation	past tense of *to draw*	to cause to move in a particular direction
trip	trip	drew	drew

Homophones	
negative response	to perceive or understand fact or truth
no	know

Homophones	
a long, narrow stretch of smooth or paved surface	past tense of *to ride*
road	rode

Homophones	
a number of things arranged in more than one line	a type of flower
rows	rose

Homophones	
short for influenza	past tense of *to fly*
flu	flew

Homophones	
to gaze	one of a flight of steps
stare	stair

Commonly Confused	
the blossom of a plant	the finely ground meal of grain
flower	flour

Heteronyms	
to shut	near
close^2	close

1. An *antonym* is a word that means the *opposite* of something else. For example, *up & down* or *big & little* are *antonyms*.

2. Read the words in the first column. Which of your spelling words are the *antonyms*? Write them in the second column.

3. Are there some left that you're not sure about? Listen as your teacher reads your spelling words to you. Write the last ones.

Antonym	Spelling Word
climbed	fell
something	nothing
elevator	stairs
sky	ground
walked	rode
center	edge
open	close
landed	flew
weren't	were
unsure	know
dropped	held
erased	drew
thorn	rose
spirit	body
weed	flower

1. Take a quiz on some single-letter phonograms in the "Letter" columns below.
2. Listen as your teacher reads your spelling words to you. Write the word next to the letter that is at the beginning of each of your spelling words.
3. If there is more than one word with the same first letter, look at the second letter to help you list them in *alphabetical* order.
4. When you're done with your quiz, your words will now be in *alphabetical* order.
5. Correct any errors.

Letter	Spelling Word	Letter	Spelling Word
b	body	g	ground
	butcher	h	held
c	climate	k	kitchen
	close		know
d	drew	n	nothing
e	edge	r	rode
f	fell		rose
	flew	s	stair
	flour	t	trip
	flower	w	were

Teacher Notes:
1. Dictate the single-letter phonograms to your student, using phonogram sounds. Have him only write in open spaces.
2. Read the List L-4 words to your student *in the order listed in the WG*. You purposely want to read them in a scrambled order (not how they're listed on this worksheet) so that he has to think about how to match the word with its first letter.
3. Demonstrate how to alphabetize based on the second letter when more than one word starts with the same letter.
Alternative way to teach alphabetizing.
   a. Dictate the spelling words to the student for a quiz, having him write each word on a 3x5 card.
   b. Correct any errors. Spread the cards out on the table upside down.
   c. Show him the alphabet on a chart or on a letter strip. Practice identifying the next three letters at any given starting point. (For example, say "L, M, N..." and he needs to finish with "O, P, Q.")
   d. Select two cards and demonstrate how to put them on the table in alphabetical order, from left to right.
   e. Select another card and add it to the first two alphabetized cards in the correct placement. Continue until you have all 20 cards in alphabetical order, from left to right.
   f. Gather the cards, keeping them in alphabetical order.
   g. Proceed with the assignment as explained above in #1-#3.
   h. Have the student read each card from his stack of cards and compare them with the words he wrote on the worksheet. They should match. He can now alphabetize words based on their first and second letters.

1. Good writers always start by planning what they will be writing about.

2. Below are three topics that you could write about using this week's spelling words.

3. Look in your Learning Log at your List L-4 words. Find four to six words that could relate to each topic and write them in that column.

4. Write a paragraph about one of these topics **OR** write a paragraph about a vacation to Paris, the land of French cooks and beautiful art.

5. A paragraph should be indented on the first line and have at least four sentences.

Vacation	Food	Art
trip	butcher	drew
rode	kitchen	held
climate	ground	rose
flew	flour	close

Teacher Notes:
1. Word suggestions are listed above but students may think of different related words or add more to these.

2. See SWR Step #23 for instructions on teaching writing.

3. Have your student brainstorm what he will write on separate paper first. Planning what to write makes writing so much easier.

4. Have him write a rough draft and edit it before rewriting it in his best penmanship on this page.

5. Putting ideas, words, correct spelling, proper grammar, *and* punctuation together is a *lot* to remember for a young student. When the student writes independently, much of the punctuation will be caught in the editing process.

1. An **antonym** is a word that means the **opposite** of something else. For example, *up & down* or *big & little* are **antonyms**.

2. Read the words in the first column. Ask for help if you don't know how to read these words. Do you know what these words mean? Discuss them with your teacher.

3. Which of your spelling words are the **opposite** of these words? Write them in the second column.

4. Correct your work.

Antonym	Spelling Word
true	false or lie
ash	coal
stop	begin
regular	express
incapable	able
himself	herself
out of style	in fashion
in spite of	because
left	right
shame	glory
nothing	anything
inherit	earn

Teacher Note: The word *lie* is not a current spelling word, but it is a reasonable answer, especially given the story that is recommended with List L-5.

1. An *analogy* is a comparison between two things.

2. Look at the first pair of words and figure out the relationship between them. Then look at the second set of words. They share the same relationship as the first two.

   Ship is to water as train is to _____track_____.

   In this example, the comparison (or the relationship) is where a vehicle belongs or travels.

3. Below are pairs of words. The first pair relate to one another in some way. How are these words related? Use that same relationship to complete the second pair.

4. Use your spelling words from this week's list to complete each set of *analogies*.

   Stove is to burner as tree is to _____leaf_____.

   Dress is to fabric as pipe is to _____lead_____.

   Dog is to fur as bird is to _____feathers_____.

   Beef is to hamburger as milk is to _____cheese_____.

   Flying is to bird as slithering is to _____worm_____.

   Right is to wrong as true is to _____false_____.

   Give is to get as pay is to _____earn_____.

1. Take a quiz on some review words, some of your new spelling words, and three new words.

2. Correct your quiz so that everything is spelled correctly.

3. Combine your spelling words with the review words to create one *compound word* for each spelling word.

Review and New Words			
able	**cloth**	down	pin
birth	**clover**	fly	ring
book	cut	over	up
cake			

Teacher Note: The words in **bold** are new. Dictate them now.

Spelling Word	Compound Word
earn	earnable
leaf	flyleaf, overleaf, cloverleaf
feather	pinfeather
right	downright, upright, birthright
cheese	cheesecake, cheesecloth
worms	bookworms, ringworms, cutworms
fashion	fashionable

4. Write a sentence using one of your new *compound words.*

Answers will vary.

Examples: The duckling lost his pinfeathers.

The older son wants his birthright.

1. A **synonym** is a word that means the same as something else. For example, *big* & *huge* and *small* & *little* are **synonyms**.

2. Read the words in the first column. Discuss with your teacher what these words mean.

3. As your teacher dictates your spelling words, match them to their **synonym** below.

4. Correct your work.

Synonym	Spelling Word
teeny	tiny
daybreak	morning
beforehand	early
mankind	people
daddy	father
prior to	before
lanky	tall
earth	world

5. Write a sentence using one of your spelling words. Then write it again using the **synonym**. The sentence should have a similar meaning.

Answers will vary.

Examples: Father went to work on Friday morning.

Daddy went to work on Friday morning.

1. The word *order* can fill two different parts of speech.

   > **noun** - a command, an array, a condition in which everything is properly disposed
   >
   > **verb** - to demand or command others, to arrange in a particular way

2. Using the **base word** *order*, add the **prefixes** and **suffixes** listed below to form **derivatives**. You can use one **prefix**, one **suffix**, or both a **prefix** and a **suffix**. You might even use two **suffixes** together.

3. Be creative, but make sure you're forming real English words. Maybe you can you find an *orderly* way to solve the puzzle.

Prefixes	
dis-	pre-
mis-	re-

Suffixes		
-able	-ing	-ness
-ed	-ly	-s

Derivatives of *order*			
order	disorder	misorderable	preordered
orderable	disorders	misorders	preordering
orders	disordered	misordered	reorder
ordered	disordering	misordering	reorderable
ordering	disorderly	preorder	reorders
orderly	disorderliness	preorderable	reordered
orderliness	misorder	preorders	reordering

Teacher Note:

1. If you haven't done so yet, make a copy of WG pp 98 & 116 and cut apart the **suffix** and **prefix cards**. Save the cards to use with **derivative** activities like this one.

2. Create a flash card for the word **order** and demonstrate how to mix and match the **suffixes** and **prefixes** with each word card to create legitimate English words.

3. The student records his findings in the chart above.

1. Take a quiz on some review words and on some of your new spelling words.

2. Correct your quiz so that everything is spelled correctly.

3. Combine your spelling words with the review words to create one *compound word* for each spelling word.

Review Words			
for	hand	more	towns
grand	land	none	under
green	lasting	star	what

Spelling Word	Compound Word
ever	evergreen, everlasting, forever, whatever, evermore
before	beforehand
morning	morningstar
father	fatherland, grandfather
people	townspeople
world	underworld

4. Write a sentence using one of your new *compound words.*

Answers will vary.

Examples: The townspeople cleaned up their home town together.

God has an everlasting love for his people.

1. We add the endings *-er* and *-est* to adjectives to express comparison.

	-er more of	**-est** the most
Mary is **tall.**	Sue is **taller** than Mary. (comparing two)	Tom is the **tallest** of all. (comparing three or more)

2. Some multi-syllable words do not change with these suffixes. Instead the adjective stays the same but has *more* or *most* in front of it.

a *careful* man	a *more careful* man	a *most careful* man

3. Take a quiz on some of your review words in the first column. Correct your work.

4. Practice adding the *-er and -est* suffixes to each word. Watch out for your rules!

5. Find four more words in List L-6 that can be made into *comparative adjectives* and add them to the page in the first column. Practice adding the *-er* and *-est* endings to these words as well.

Positive Degree Spelling Word - Adjective	**Comparative Degree** "more than" with *-er*	**Superlative Degree** the "most" with *-est*
round	rounder	roundest
evil	more evil	most evil
clean	cleaner	cleanest
high	higher	highest
poor	poorer	poorest
mad	madder	maddest
easy	easier	easiest
warm	warmer	warmest
watery	more watery	most watery
clear	clearer	clearest
early	earlier	earliest
small	smaller	smallest
tiny	tinier	tiniest
tall	taller	tallest

Teacher Notes:
1. Only dictate the words in the first column that are in **bold. Stop** at the solid line.
2. The student is to find the last four words in his Learning Log, add them to the list, and add the *-er* and *-est* suffixes.

Wise Guide
Enrichment Activity
Worksheets

Lists M-1 to M-7

1. Write your review spelling words below as your teacher dictates them.

2. Practice using these words in your writing so that you can spell them quickly and correctly.

Teacher Notes:

1. Incorporated into the lesson plans for Wise Lists M & N are review activities for Lists A-I. These early lists include over 50% of the words we read and write, so long-term mastery of them is important!

2. Each Wise List has a two-page spread. Look for the "Review Words from A-I" activities at the top of the right-hand page for that list.

3. You'll give a quick quiz on those words. You can do the quiz on lined paper or on one of the "Review Words" Worksheets included in this book. This helps you do the review quiz AND get a new language arts activity started.

4. Any words the student misses on the quiz will then be dictated with full spelling dictation (see SWR pp 69-76) onto copies you make of this page. You'll recognize the format is similar to the Primary Learning Log, with room for parts of letters to go below the baseline without interfering with the word below it.

5. Each week, have your student add any new review words to this page and keep it in his Language Arts binder to study. You can add to it each time you teach new review words. These words should show up on the end-of-the week tests and on daily warm-up quizzes.

6. For more information on this valuable review, see WG pg 83.

1. Write your review spelling words below as your teacher dictates them.

2. Practice using these words in your writing so that you can spell them quickly and correctly.

Teacher Notes:

1. Incorporated into the lesson plans for Wise Lists M & N are review activities for Lists A-I. These early lists include over 50% of the words we read and write, so long-term mastery of them is important!

2. Each Wise List has a two-page spread. Look for the "Review Words from A-I" activities at the top of the right-hand page for that list.

3. You'll give a quick quiz on those words. You can do the quiz on lined paper or on one of the "Review Words" Worksheets included in this book. This helps you do the review quiz AND get a new language arts activity started.

4. Any words the student misses on the quiz will then be dictated with full spelling dictation (see SWR pp 69-76) onto copies you make of this page. You'll recognize the format is similar to the Black Learning Log, so have your student skip the shaded lines.

5. Each week, have your student add any new review words to this page and keep it in his Language Arts binder to study. You can add to it each time you teach new review words. These words should show up on the end-of-the week tests and on daily warm-up quizzes.

6. For more information on this valuable review, see WG pg 83.

1. Take a quiz on some single-letter phonograms in the white spaces of the "Letter" columns below.

2. Listen as your teacher reads your review words and your spelling words to you. Write the word next to the letter that is at the beginning of each of your spelling words.

3. If there is more than one word with the same first letter, look at the next several letters to help you list all of the words starting with that letter in *alphabetical* order.

4. When you're done with your quiz, your words will now be in *alphabetical* order.

5. Correct any errors.

Letter	Spelling Word	Letter	Spelling Word	Letter	Spelling Word
a	and	g	goes	r	red
	apple		green		robe
b	black	h	hair	s	sea
	blue		heaven		sew
	but		hotel		snow
c	change		house		soil
	changeable	i	ice		stone
	changing	k	key	t	thread
	color	l	lake	w	wheel
	corn	m	milk		white
d	door	o	or		who
	dough		orange	y	yellow
f	forest	p	paper		
			pencil		
			plant		
			purple		

Teacher Notes:

1. Dictate the single-letter phonograms to your student, using phonogram sounds. Have him skip gray spaces.

2. For an alternative way to teach alphabetizing, see the instructions on the *List L-4 Alphabetize* worksheet.

Teacher Notes (con't):

3. Read the List M-1 words to your student *in the order listed at the bottom of WG pg 84 and at the top of WG pg 85*. You purposely want to read them in a scrambled order (not how they're listed on this worksheet) so that he has to think about how to match the word with the letter that is at the beginning.

4. Demonstrate how to alphabetize based on the next several letters when more than one word starts with the same letter.

146

1. The cars on a train are joined together by *couplers*. Sentences use *couplers* also; they are called *conjunctions*.

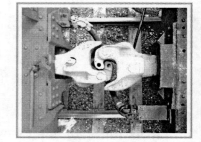

2. A *conjunction* is a word that connects words or group of words in a sentence. Some common *conjunctions* include:

    and   adds two or more items together (peanut butter *and* jelly)

    but   contrasts one idea with another (peanut butter *but* not jelly)

    or   links two things that cannot be together (peanut butter *or* jelly)

3. Use words from List M-1 to write _____ sentences with *conjunctions*.

4. (Circle) your conjunctions.

Teacher Note:
Select the number of sentences your student is to write and add that to the instructions.

Answers will vary.

   Examples: My color wheel has yellow (and) orange next to one another.

             I wanted to have a key for the hotel room, (but) I have to be ten years old first.

             I will sew with purple (or) green thread next time.

Color _____ Wheel _____

1. When you're coloring or painting, all the colors you need can come from three basic colors.

2. Write the words on the title lines below as your teacher dictates two categories of colors.

3. List the colors in each set and the two other colors that don't belong in either of these sets.

4. Write the color names in the circle, following your teacher's instructions.

5. Color your wheel and mix the colors as needed. Use crayons, colored pencils, or water colors.

6. What do we call this? Write the title at the top of the page as your teacher dictates it to you.

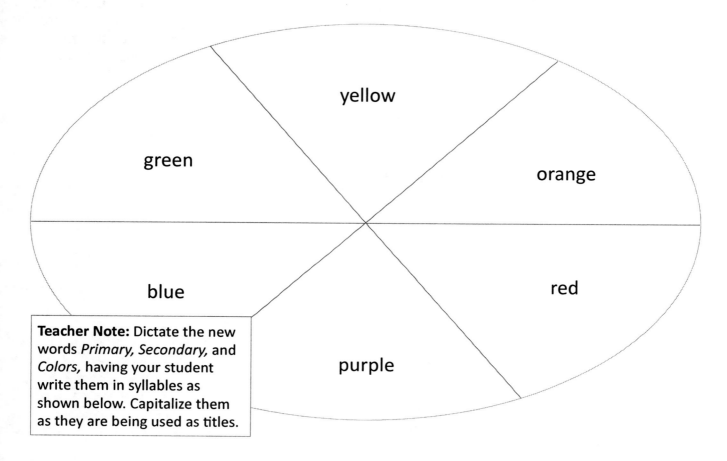

yellow

green

orange

blue

red

purple

Teacher Note: Dictate the new words _Primary, Secondary,_ and _Colors,_ having your student write them in syllables as shown below. Capitalize them as they are being used as titles.

Pri ma ry Col ors:

yellow

red

blue

black

white

Sec on da ry Col ors:

orange

purple

green

1. Take a quiz on some of your new spelling words.

2. Correct your quiz so that everything is spelled correctly.

3. Combine your spelling words with the *suffixes* below to create one *derivative* for each spelling word. Watch out for some E's Dropping and 1-1-1 words!

Suffixes	
-ed	-er
-en	-ing

Spelling Word	Derivative
stole	stolen
pass	passing, passed
account	accounted, accounting
ticket	ticketed, ticketing, ticketer
spot	spotted, spotter, spotting
angle	angled, angler, angling
sight	sighted, sighter, sighting, sighter

4. Write a sentence using one of your new *derivatives.*

Answers will vary.

Examples: She got a ticket for passing the a car in the left lane.

The scouts sighted a rare bird on the far tree.

1. Take a quiz on some review words, some of your new spelling words, and a new word.

2. Correct your quiz so that everything is spelled correctly.

3. Combine your spelling words with one another and with the review words to create one *compound word* for each spelling word. Sometimes have to add a *suffix* to make a real English word.

Review Words				
bag	eye	hope	over	under
be	far	house	port*	up
care	hand	in	shore	water
cut	head	light	sides	with
down	home	out	sun	word

Spelling Word	Compound Word
paid	overpaid, underpaid
break	breakdown, breakwater, outbreak
hold	behold, household, uphold, withhold
stood	understood, withstood
heard	overheard
pass	overpass, passover, password
less	careless, headless, homeless, hopeless
money	moneybag
spot	spotless, spotlight, sunspot
sight	eyesight, farsighted,** insight, oversight, sightless
off	cutoff, offhand, offsides, offshore

Teacher Note:
*This word has not been taught on its own, but *report* was taught in List J-3.
**Add the *ED ending* to make this derivative.

1. Take a quiz on some of your new spelling words in the "Spelling Word" columns. Correct your work.

2. The words you wrote are all *action verbs*. Combine these words with the *suffix -er* to create a *derivative* that is now a *noun* and that names a person or thing that does that action.

3. One of your words needs the *suffix -or* instead of *-er.*

4. Watch out for some E's Dropping and 1-1-1 words!

5. Play one of these games with a partner.

   a. One person reads one of the *derivatives*. The other person explains what that person or thing does. For example, for the derivative *holder,* you would answer, "A *holder* holds."

   b. Take turns acting out each of the *derivatives* while the other person tries to guess what the "person" or "thing" is doing.

Spelling Word	Derivative	Spelling Word	Derivative
swirl	swirler	attack	attacker
follow	follower	dress	dresser
provide	provider	steam	steamer
build	builder	shop	shopper
recover	recoverer	file	filer
return	returner	contract	contractor*
teach	teacher	drill	driller
speak	speaker	pitch	pitcher
praise	praiser	swim	swimmer
solve	solver	fix	fixer

Teacher Note: See WG pg 88 for an explanation about the Latin-based word *contractor.**

1. Take a quiz on some review words in the first column below. Correct your work.

2. Combine your spelling words with the *suffixes* below to create a *derivative* for each word.

3. Watch out for the 1-1-1 rule!

Suffixes		
-ed	-en	-ing
-er	-est	-y

Review Words	Derivative
run	runner, running
top	topped, topping, topper
cut	cutting, cutter
cat	catty
let	letting
pet	petted, petty, petting
roll	roller, rolled, rolling
dog	dogged, doggy
bog	boggy
row	rowing, rowed, rower
flat	flattest, flatter, flatten, flattened, flattening
step	stepping, stepped, stepper
put	putting
end	ending, ended, ender
fun	funny, funnest, funnier, funniest

Teacher Note: Some derivatives with the *-en suffix* can have other *suffixes* added as well.

Teacher Note: To make this word into the comparative form, we add *-er* or *-est* to the *derivative funny*. This uses the Y's Exchanging Rule, which may not have been introduced yet. See SWR pg 167.

1. Every sentence must have these two parts.
    subject   telling what or who the sentence is about
    verb   telling something about the subject

    The little girl ran down the street.   Who is the sentence about?   girl - **subject**
                                                What about the [**subject**]?   ran - **verb**

2. Listen as your teacher dictates your new spelling words in **subject-verb** pairs and write the words in the appropriate columns. Watch out for the E's Dropping and 1-1-1 Rules!

3. Correct your quiz so that everything is spelled correctly.

4. Taking turns with a partner, read your word pairs and tell the other person a sentence for each set of words. Write your sentences on the Grammar - Subject & Verbs Sentences Worksheet.

Subject	Verb
shopper	pitched
dress	swirled
follower	solved
attack	swirled
builder	contracted
attack	followed
speaker	filed
provider	recovered
pitch	steams
teacher	praises
swimmer	recovered
teacher	drills
shop	returns
drill	provided
attacker	fixed
shopper	returns

1. Write _____ sentences using your ***subject & verb pairs*** that you wrote on the Subject & Verb Worksheet.

2. Use spelling words from M-3. Underline your spelling words.

Teacher Note: Select the number of sentences your student is to write and add that to the instructions.

Answers will vary.

Examples: Our teacher drills us on arithmetic every day.

A builder contracted to do the work by Saturday.

1. An *analogy* is a comparison between two things.

2. Look at the first pair of words and figure out the relationship between them. Then look at the second set of words. They share the same relationship as the first two.

> Ship is to water as train is to _____track_____.

> In this example, the comparison (or the relationship) is where a vehicle belongs or travels.

3. Below are pairs of words. The first pair relate to one another in some way. How are these words related? Use that same relationship to complete the second pair.

4. Use your spelling words from this week's list to complete each set of *analogies*.

Quiet is to loud as silence is to _____noise_____.

Swim is to walk as navy is to _____army_____.

See is to hear as lightning is to _____thunder_____.

Low is to high as valleys are to _____mountains_____.

Forward is to backward as push is to _____pull_____.

Father is to sons as parent is to _____children_____.

Evening is to morning as supper is to _____breakfast_____.

Washing machine is to clothes as lawn mower is to _____grass_____.

Spaghetti noodle is to lasagne noodle as narrow is to _____broad_____.

Bed is to ladder as sleep is to _____climb_____.

Ceiling is to floor as above is to _____below_____.

1. Take a quiz on some of your new spelling words.

2. Correct your quiz so that everything is spelled correctly.

3. Combine your spelling words with the *suffixes* to create one *derivative* for each spelling word.

4. Watch out for some E's Dropping and Y's Exchanging words!

Suffixes			
-ed	-er	-ing	-ness
-en	-es	-ly	-s

Spelling Word	Derivative
climb	climbs, climbed, climber, climbing
happen	happens, happened, happening
monkey	monkeys, monkeyed, monkeying
ready	readies, readiness, readying, readied
thunder	thunders, thundering, thundered
picture	pictures, pictured, picturing
pull	pulls, pulled, pulling
broad	broader, broaden, broadly
eagle	eagles
army	armies

5. Write a sentence using one of your new *derivatives*.

Answers will vary.

Examples: He pulled himself up the ladder.

It was thundering hard in the storm last night.

Use your new spelling words and an NIV Bible to complete the List M-5 Cross-Word Puzzle.

Down

1. At harvest time he sent a servant to the tenants to __collect__ from them some of the fruit of the vineyard. (Mark 12:2)

3. A __truthful__ witness saves lives, but a false witness is deceitful. (Proverbs 14:25)

6. "I __regret__ that I have made Saul king, because he has turned away from me and has not carried out my instructions." (1 Samuel 15:11)

8. I lie down and sleep; I wake __again__, because the Lord sustains me. (Psalm 3:5)

9. Praise be to the Lord, to God our Savior, who __daily__ bears our burdens. (Psalm 68:19)

10. While they were there, the time came for the baby to be __born__. (Luke 2:6)

11. Praise our God, all peoples, let the __sound__ of His praise be heard. (Psalm 66:8)

12. Then Moses and Aaron were __driven__ out of Pharaoh's presence. (Exodus 10:11b)

16. The fool __says__ in his heart, "There is no God." (Psalm 14:1a)

Across

2. "__Enter__ through the narrow gate." (Matthew 7:13a)

4. The day is yours, and yours __also__ the night; you established the sun and moon. Psalm 74:16

5. But as for me, my feet had __almost__ slipped; I had nearly lost my foothold. (Psalm 73:2)

7. I will praise you with an upright heart as I __learn__ your righteous laws. (Psalm 119:7)

9. For what I received I passed on to you as of first importance: that Christ __died__ for our sins according to the Scriptures, that he was buried, that he was raised on the third day according to the Scriptures. (1 Corinthians 15:3-4)

11. I gave you milk, not __solid__ food, for you were not yet ready for it. Indeed, you are still not ready. (1 Corinthians 3:2)

13. Very __rarely__ will anyone die for a righteous person, though for a good person someone might possibly dare die. (Romans 5:7)

14. "I am the __true__ vine, and my Father is the gardener." (John 15:1)

15. For God __does__ not show favoritism. (Romans 2:11)

17. By the twenty-seventh day of the second __month__ the earth was completely dry. (Genesis 8:14)

18. "A farmer went out to __sow__ his seed." (Matthew 13:3b)

See the instructions on page 157.

```
                              1 c            2 e  n  3 t  e  r
              4 a  l  s         o                   r
                                l                   u
                        5 a  l  m  o  s              t
                                e                   h
                                c                   f
                                t                   u
                        6 r              7 l  e  8 a  r  n
                  9 d  i  e  d                     g
                     a        g                    a
        10 b        i        r        11 s  o  l  i  d
           o     12 d        e           o        n
        13 r  a  r  e  l  y        14 t  r  u  e
           n     i                    n
                 v                15 d  o  e  16 s
                 e                           a
        17 m  o  n  t  h                     y
                                        18 s  o  w
```

1. Take a quiz on some of your review words.

2. Correct your quiz so that everything is spelled correctly.

3. Write _____ sentences, using at least one adverb from your list in each one.

4. (Circle) your adverbs and <u>underline</u> your spelling words.

Teacher Notes: Select the number of sentences your student is to write and add that to the instructions.

Adverbs				
as	here	not	soon	very
away	just	now	then	when
ever	never	so	today	yet

Answers will vary.

Examples: He <u>does</u> his <u>collec</u>tions (almost) daily but (never) on a Sunday.

She may (not) <u>enter</u> the home (today.)

1. Write the *adjectives* your teacher dictates in the "Adjectives" column below and the word pairs in the "Spelling Word Pairs" column.

2. Correct your work so that everything is spelled correctly.

3. *Adverbs* are words that
    a. can be used to modify or describe *verbs*, *adjectives*, or other *adverbs*
    b. can hide in different places in a sentence, but are often before or after the *verb*
    c. can end with the *suffix -ly* but don't always
    d. answer these questions: *how?*   *where?*   *when?*   *how often?*   *to what extent?*

4. Write each of these words again with the *-ly suffix* in the "Adverbs" column. Watch out for any spelling rules that need to be used.

5. Look at the first column of your Learning Log where you'll find the *adjectives* you wrote below. Find the spelling word that is across from each of these words in your Learning Log and write it next to your new *-ly adverbs* to create an *adverb phrase.*

6. Which of the questions above is answered by the *adverb* in each of your word *adverb phrases*? Write these in the "Question" column for both charts.

Adjectives	Adverbs	Question
month	monthly sow	how often
sound	soundly does	how
true	truly says	how
truthful	truthfully driven	how
solid	solidly learn	how

Spelling Word Pairs		Question
almost born		to what extent
again enter	**Teacher Note:** Dictate to your student the *adjectives* and *adverb* word pairs that are shown here in **bold**. He can complete the rest of the page independently or with your assistance.	when
almost died		to what extent
daily regrets		when
rarely collect		how often

1. Read these sentences.   *Mother got something. Mother read a book. Listen to Mother.*
    Do you hear Mother reading? Thank you, Mother.

2. Saying "Mother" over and over and over can get tiring, so we use ***pronouns*** instead. Doesn't this sound better?

    Mother got something. She read a book. Listen to her.
    Do you hear her reading? Thank you, Mother.

3. Use the sample sentences to fill in the Pronoun chart below.

    _____ *will run.*   *Tom saw* _____.   *This is* _____ *book.*   *That book is* _____.

Singular Pronouns

Person		Subjective	Objective	Possessive	
1st		I	me	my	mine
2nd		you	you	your	yours
3rd	M	he	him	his	his
	F	she	her	her	hers
	N	it	it	its	its

Plural Pronouns

Person	Subjective	Objective	Possessive		
1st	we	us	our	ours	
2nd	you	you	your	yours	*Advanced Option (see List Q-6)
3rd	they	them	their*	theirs*	

Teacher Note: *Pronouns* tell us four things about the noun they're replacing.

a. **Person:** 1st person - person speaking
2nd person - person being spoken to
3rd person - person being spoken about

b. **Gender:** Masculine (males)
Feminine (females)
Neuter (neither one)   *(Only 3rd person singular pronouns use gender.)*

c. **Number:** singular (one)
plural (more than one)

d. **Case:** subject - person/thing doing the action
object - person/thing receiving the action

1. Take a quiz on words from List M-6, writing them on the first line of each box below.

2. Correct your work to be sure everything is spelled correctly.

3. Each of these words can be used as a *noun*, a word for a person, a place, a thing, or an idea.

4. Think of two more nouns to write on the last two lines.

5. Look in your Learning Log for words from List M-6 that could be *adjectives* or words that describe nouns. Using these words, write three *adjective & noun* combinations on the lines below each of your nouns.

finger	chance	heart
Answers will vary. Examples:		
middle finger		
those fingers		

phrase	case	chick

event	collar	railroad

member	Answers will vary.	Answers will vary.

1. Write _____ sentences using your *adjective & noun* combinations that you wrote on the Adjective Worksheet.

2. Underline your spelling words.

Answers will vary.

   Examples: My brother has a narrow finger.

              You say the middle phrase, and I will say the rest.

1. The word *oxymoron* comes from the Greek language. *oxys* = "sharp"   *moros* = "stupid"

2. An *oxymoron* is a figure of speech in which two words which are *opposites* are used together.

    shrimp means "something small"   >   *jumbo shrimp = an* **oxymoron**
    jumbo means "large"

3. Can you explain these *oxymorons*?

    small giant   good grief   wise fool   tight slacks
    empty spot   almost exactly   soft rock   almost done

4. Use your List M-7 spelling words to complete the following *oxymorons*.

easy _____hurdle_____

terribly _____pleased_____

bad _____deal_____

_____bury_____ a find

spent _____income_____

blank _____record_____

blind _____stare_____

_____gentle_____ jolt

_____pretty_____ ugly

_____understand_____ a puzzle

Teacher Note:
This activity involves higher level language skills, so your student will likely need your assist-ance. Refer to the tips on WG pg 96 for how to guide your student in understanding these *oxymorons*.

1. Take a quiz on some review words and on some of your new spelling words.

2. Correct your quiz so that everything is spelled correctly.

3. Combine your spelling words with the *prefixes* to create one *derivative* for each spelling word. Two of the words cannot mix with the *prefixes* to form a *derivative*. Which ones are they?

Prefixes					
anti-	*against*	**mis-**	*wrong* or *bad*	**re-**	*again*
dis-	*the opposite*	**out-**	*away* or *more*	**super-**	*over* or *above*
in-	*in* or *opposite of*	**over-**	*higher / too much*	**un-**	*not / opposite of*

Review Words	Derivative
easy	uneasy
day*	
find	refind
form	reform, inform, misinform, uninformed
heat	overheat, reheat
told	retold, untold
make	remake
cold	overcold
see	oversee
like	dislike, unlike

Review Words	Derivative
live	outlive
lay	mislay, outlay, overlay
led	misled
look	outlook, overlook
man	superman
miss	dismiss, remiss
Miss	
spent	outspent, overspent, unspent
zip	unzip

TEACHER NOTE:
*If your student suggests "super day," let him know this is an *adjective + noun phrase*, not a *compound word*.

1. Take a quiz on your new spelling words. Correct your quiz so that everything is spelled correctly.

2. Combine your spelling words with the *prefixes* to create one *derivative* for each spelling word. Some of your words could use the *suffix -ed* to make a real word.

3. Two of the words cannot mix with the *prefixes* to form a *derivative*. Which ones are they?

Prefixes					
anti-	*against*	*mis-*	*wrong* or *bad*	*re-*	*again*
dis-	*the opposite*	*out-*	*away* or *more*	*super-*	*over* or *above*
in-	*in* or *opposite of*	*over-*	*higher / too much*	*un-*	*not / opposite of*

Spelling Words	Derivative
inform	misinform, uninformed*
furnish	refurnish, unfurnished*
charge	discharge, overcharge, recharge, supercharge
freeze	antifreeze, unfreeze
took	overtook, mistook
trust	distrust, mistrust
fasten	refasten, unfasten
bought	overbought, unbought, rebought
laid	mislaid, outlaid, overlaid, relaid
able**	unable

Spelling Words	Derivative
hurdle	
deal	redeal
come**	income
please	displease
record	misrecord, unrecorded*
stare	outstare
gentle	ungentle
bury	unbury, rebury
pretty***	
understand	misunderstand

Teacher Note:
*Add *suffix -ed* to form an English *derivative*.
**Dictate the *base word* so that the student can add a prefix to create the spelling word.
***If the student suggests "super pretty," let him know this is an *adjective + noun phrase*, not a *compound word*.

1. Take a quiz on some of your new spelling words. Correct your work.

2. Combine your spelling words with the **suffixes -ing** and **-er** to create **derivatives**.

3. You'll need to use the E's Dropping and Y's Exchanging rules to form some of these **derivatives**.

4. Four of the words cannot have the **suffix -er** added and still form a true derivative. Which ones are they?

Spelling Words	-ing	-er
furnish	furnishing	furnisher
break	breaking	breaker
fasten	fastening	fastener
income	incoming	incomer
stare	staring	
understand	understanding	
inform	informing	informer
freeze	freezing	freezer
hurdle	hurdling	hurdler
please	pleasing	pleaser
bury	burying	
charge	charging	charger
trust	trusting	
deal	dealing	dealer
record	recording	recorder
pretty	prettying	prettier

CPSIA information can be obtained
at www.ICGtesting.com
Printed in the USA
FSOW02n0217260516
20820FS